TABLE OF CONTENTS

Due to all inhabitants of the world's good karma,
this beautiful planet was created. But if it's all covered up
by the new bad karma, then the planet and/or
the inhabitants will perish.

Make good karma:
Be Loving
Be Veg
Be Green

—Supreme Master Ching Hai

FOREWORD

At conferences, in interviews with journalists and at gatherings with disciples in recent years, Supreme Master Ching Hai has spoken with increasing urgency about Earth's current climate crisis. As she states, "Our planet is a house that is burning. If we don't work together with a united spirit to put out the fire, we will not have a home anymore." But she also offers humankind an uplifting solution, one that every individual can easily achieve: "Be veg to save the planet."

As the crisis escalates, natural disasters are claiming tens of thousands of lives and displacing millions from their homes, with financial losses amounting to billions of dollars. Rising sea levels have already submerged many islands and are threatening the existence of several island nations. In addition, irregular rainfall patterns and intensifying droughts are affecting many regions, thus worsening food and water shortages. And climate experts warn of even more extreme weather conditions to come, with the possibility of "runaway global warming."

In this book Supreme Master Ching Hai presents the major factors associated with global warming, and more importantly, its root cause: the livestock industry.

In fact, many scientific studies support Supreme Master Ching Hai's view, which she has expounded for over twenty years. The raising of animals for food not only wastes massive amounts of precious water, land and energy, but also contributes to a staggering 51% of the planet's greenhouse gas emissions. Livestock farming is also the greatest single source of atmospheric methane, a much more powerful greenhouse gas than CO_2, but one with a shorter lifespan.

Thus, as Supreme Master Ching Hai says, it is only logical that halting meat production and "becoming veg" or adopting a plant-based diet will immediately reduce global temperatures, heal the environmental ills caused by livestock and reduce the costs of mitigating climate change by trillions of dollars. Also, such a shift can achieve these results with virtually no negative impact on the planet and society. In contrast, similar cuts in the carbon dioxide produced by industry and the transport sector could have devastating economic effects. Furthermore, most green technologies take years to develop, while cuts in methane emissions can be achieved immediately with every vegan meal. So adopting the vegan lifestyle is the easiest, quickest and least costly solution to the climate crisis, and it is also our only salvation because we are running out of time.

Many climate experts, environmentalists and government officials have already begun advocating this approach to saving the earth from the worst effects of climate change. Their voices culminated in the June 2010 United Nations report urging a global transition to a meat- and dairy-free diet, echoing Supreme Master Ching Hai's urgent plea: **Everyone who has decision-making power should take the courageous step to enact laws that immediately facilitate this shift.**

Perhaps even more devastating than our carbon footprints that have caused the climate crisis are the bloody footprints we leave behind in slaughtering billions of innocent farm animals each year. Supreme Master warns that this moral crime has reached global proportions, as our violent acts come back to us in the form of natural disasters: "As you sow, so shall you reap." Such is the universal teaching found in all the world's great scriptures.

Indeed, humankind is facing a crucial turning point. We have only one chance to save the planet and the time is now. Simply by adopting the benevolent, life-saving, plant-based diet we can dispel the darkness engulfing us. And this small step will in turn propel humankind into a higher level of consciousness. We will restore harmony to planet Earth and thus usher in the Golden Era of peace, beauty and love. As Supreme Master Ching Hai promises, we will then have Heaven on Earth.

Let us all seize the opportunity and make the change today. Let us all choose to evolve and elevate our civilization and the planet.

Notes from the Editors:

This book contains unabridged excerpts from Supreme Master's talks at international conferences and gatherings with disciples, as well as from interviews with journalists. For references to these sources, please refer to "Bibliography of Talks by Supreme Master Ching Hai" on page 145.

In speaking of God or the Absolute, Supreme Master Ching Hai uses the following gender-neutral terms to avoid arguments about whether God is male or female.

She + He = Hes (as in Bless)
Her + Him = Hirm (as in Firm)
Hers + His = Hiers (as in Dears)

Example: When God wants, Hes makes things
happen according to Hiers will to suit Hirmself.

As a creator of artistic designs as well as a spiritual teacher, Supreme Master Ching Hai loves all expressions of inner beauty. It is for this reason that she refers to Vietnam as "Au Lac" and Taiwan as "Formosa." Au Lac is the ancient name of Vietnam and it means "happiness." And the name of Formosa, meaning "beautiful," reflects more completely the beauty of the island and its people. Master feels that using these names brings spiritual elevation and luck to the land and its inhabitants.

A Brief Biography of Supreme Master Ching Hai

Supreme Master Ching Hai is a world-renowned humanitarian, environmentalist, author, artist, designer, musician, film director and spiritual teacher, whose love and care for humanity extend beyond all racial and national boundaries. Since the early 1980s she has also been one of our planet's most dedicated ecological pioneers, promoting environmental protection, biodiversity preservation, reforestation, sustainable living and most importantly, the organic vegan diet, the quickest, most effective way to solve the climate crisis.

With unwavering determination, she devotes her time and resources to awakening the world to the disastrous impact of climate change and to the vegan solution. From 2006 to 2008 she launched the Alternative Living and SOS global-warming-awareness campaigns and inspired the founding of Loving Hut, the world's fastest-growing, international vegan restaurant chain by the Supreme Master Ching Hai International Association, an NGO begun through her example. She also publishes a news magazine, writes books, produced the 2005 vegetarian documentary The Real Heroes and the TV series *The King & Co.*, broadcast on Supreme Master Television, a 24/7, global satellite channel offering news on climate change, the vegan diet and other uplifting topics. Since 2007 Master Ching Hai has also shared her knowledge with environmental experts, government leaders, VIPs and concerned citizens through over 29 climate-change conferences in 15 countries broadcast live on satellite TV and radio. As a result of these efforts, her motto "Be Veg, Go Green 2 Save the Planet" has spread around the globe, inspiring humankind to embrace the healthy, sustainable vegan lifestyle and thus evolve into a higher state of peace and harmony. Through her kind example, Supreme Master Ching Hai also reminds us of our inner goodness and love for all of God's creations. The profound insights she gained through her spiritual attainment allowed her to identify the root cause of human suffering, social discord and environmental degradation: the violence we inflict on other beings, including our innocent animal friends. Out of compassion for the weak and voiceless, Supreme Master Ching Hai thus wrote the #1 international bestsellers *The Birds in My Life, The Dogs in My Life, and The Noble Wilds*. These literary gems, available in various languages, reveal the deep thoughts and feelings of our treasured animal co-inhabitants, highlighting their divine nature and unconditional love.

Born in central Au Lac (Vietnam), Supreme Master Ching Hai studied in Europe and worked for the Red Cross. She soon realized that suffering exists in all corners of the globe, and her yearning to find a remedy became the foremost goal in her life. She then embarked on a journey to the Himalayas in search of spiritual enlightenment and eventually received divine transmission of the inner Light and Sound, which she later called the Quan Yin Method. After a period of diligent practice, Supreme Master Ching Hai attained the Great Enlightenment. Soon after her return from the Himalayas, at the request of those around her, Supreme Master Ching Hai began sharing the Quan Yin Method, encouraging her students to look within to find their own divine greatness. Before long, she received invitations to give lectures in the Americas, Europe, Asia, Australia and Africa. Supreme Master Ching Hai's compassionate heart is also reflected in her care for the less fortunate. Funds generated from the sale of her artistic creations have enabled her to support her mission of comforting God's children in need through worldwide disaster relief and charity work.

Although she seeks no acknowledgement for her humanitarian work, Supreme Master Ching Hai has received numerous awards from governments and private organizations around the world, including the World Peace Award, the World Spiritual Leadership Award, the Award for Promotion of Human Rights, the World Citizen Humanitarian Award, the Award for Outstanding Public Service to Mankind, the 2006 Gusi Peace Prize, the Los Angeles Music Week Certificate of Commendation, First

Place Silver for the 27th Annual Telly Awards 2006, the Presidential Active Lifestyle Award from former US President George W. Bush, and the 2010 President's Volunteer Service Award from US President Barack Obama.

In addition, October 25 and February 22 were proclaimed "Supreme Master Ching Hai Day" in the US by government officials in Hawaii and Illinois. Congratulatory messages were sent to her during the Illinois proclamation ceremony by former US Presidents Clinton, Bush and Reagan. And to commend virtuous individuals and encourage others to be inspired by their examples, Supreme Master Ching Hai has also created the Shining World Awards series, recognizing deserving humans and animals for exceptional heroism, compassion, leadership, bravery or intelligence.

Supreme Master Ching Hai thus selflessly dedicates her life to creating a beautiful future for our beloved planet and its precious co-inhabitants. Throughout history great visionaries have had dreams, and Supreme Master Ching Hai expresses hers as follows: "I have a dream. I dream that all the world will become peaceful. I dream that all the killing will stop. I dream that all the children will walk in peace and harmony. I dream that all the nations shake hands with each other, protect each other and help each other. I dream that our beautiful planet will not be destroyed. It takes billion, billion, trillions of years to produce this planet and it's so beautiful, so wonderful. I dream that it will continue, but in peace, beauty and love."

How I really want to embrace the leaders and the non-leaders, people of this world and tell them, "Wake up." I want to embrace them and tell them, "Wake up, wake up now. Wake up, my love; wake up my friend, save yourself."

A PERSONAL PLEA FROM SUPREME MASTER CHING HAI TO WORLD LEADERS

I am very grateful to the courageous leaders in the world for stepping out of their boundary and speaking out for the sake of everyone. Even if the public does not appreciate their goodwill, Heaven will take note. And they will have a great reward hereafter. It is, of course, very difficult to be in the position of authority.

To be a leader is to be endowed with bravery, compassion and nobility. That's why you are a leader. It's not easy, of course, to be in the position of a leader. That's why leaders are few. In a nation, there's only one king, one queen, some princesses, some princes, one president, one prime minister: very few leaders compared to the multitude of this world. But fewer even still are brave leaders, courageous leaders, righteous leaders and wise leaders.

To such a wise and courageous one, we offer full support and respect. We pray that Heaven give them more strength, more wisdom to carry out their noble duty. Because as I told you, leaders are few. And fewer still are those who are wise and courageous. Being a leader, we must know what is good for our subjects and what is not. And what is good, we have to encourage them to do, facilitate them to do. And what is bad, we have to stop, to protect them. That is the true meaning of a leader.

Promote the Animal-Free Lifestyle that Benefits All People

The best government should promote policies which benefit the ordinary people and all people. To be effective, governments now must realize that this is a special, special situation, one that requires exceptional measures.

I suggest all world leaders and governments to please promote the animal-free lifestyle and quick so that we can save our planet.

We have no time, not too much time left. This is no longer even about politics. It's about the survival of ourselves and our children. If all governments encourage people toward the healthy, animal-free diet, the planet could be saved in no time.

The activities that are good for our Earth can also generate livelihood. We have a shortage of food, so the government can easily support organic vegan farmers and the advancement of other green practices. This will help greatly. The government must make a priority, saving the planet, organic farming, subsidize.

To all the leaders, I call on them once more to put their love first for their countrymen and women, and for all the children to accept with courage the deed that must be done, to use the mighty power in their hands entrusted by people to save the world.

The global livestock industry is now contributing almost about as much to global warming as the energy sector, or even more. And I know it contributes at least 80% of it. Meat production is depleting your people's water, damaging their health, pushing them to war and breeding new deadly disease each day.

It's killing your people. Only you can stop it.

They need your shining, heroic, vegan example because they really look to their governments, to their leaders.

They would be greatly facilitated by your laws for organic vegan farming and campaigns or laws to make the much needed lifestyle vegan change.

Your co-citizens, your subjects, will appreciate you, praise you, love you, support you and they will remember you for saving the world for generations to come even, for saving their lives and the lives of their loved ones, as well as their future children. And Heaven will reward you greatly.

Lead the veg change. Promote forgiveness and peace and then even all other troubles, like poverty, conflict, even financial crisis, pandemics, will also subside.

I thank you, leaders of nations, for all the efforts in this direction so far.

We Are All Part of the Solution

But if you allow me, I honestly say that what we are doing and planning now is not enough, and not fast enough and I bid you the courage and faith to do more and faster.

To the organizations of the world, including the media who understand the strength of a social movement, thank you for your work to inform and encourage people to the exciting and humane, beneficial, chic, animal-free—the vegan way of life.

To the individuals, thank you for doing your part to save our planet, but please, to make it in time, we have more to do and we have little time.

We have to continue to urge our leaders and our fellow human beings, neighbors to change, be vegan to save themselves and their families and children and the animals, and everything they feel is worth living for.

We can get out of the danger but through the right direction. Our house is on fire but the water hose is right there in front of us.

Just pick it up and use it; it's as simple as that. Just be vegan. And please be quick. Our days are numbered.

To all humankind, Heaven loves you so much. So we have hope for the planet's survival, more than ever before. We shall awaken to a new, compassionate, vegan planet that is full of loving energy, kindness and blessings no end from Heaven.

I pray you all will continue towards this peace in our reach. Thank you so much, all of you. Thank you.

> If everybody stops eating meat right now, within eight weeks' time, the weather will change into a benevolent one. Everything that has been damaged will be returned to normal in eight weeks' time. If everybody on the planet stopped eating meat and turned into compassionate heart, then the result will be immediate.

We can still save the planet

Day 694*

Be Vegan

−Supreme Master Ching Hai

*Supreme Master Ching Hai has compassionately stated, through her profound spiritual knowledge, that this is the time world citizens have left to save the planet. We pray that when we reach the 0 count, we will have a glorious, compassionate vegan Earth, in which all beings live in harmony.

*Day count as of March 1, 2011

1

THE VEGAN SOLUTION TO SAVE THE WORLD

Right now, it's urgent. We have to stop global warming in order to survive first. So, vegan is the only solution for immediate overall effect for all problems of the environment, survival, health, the economy, etc., on our planet.

I do believe that our planet is on the threshold of constructive change for the better of all inhabitants, including animals and trees and plants.

If we take this opportunity to work together in changing our bad habits, like the meat-eating, the drug-taking, the cigarette-smoking, the alcohol abusing, then in the same way that many nations have stopped the smoking habit, we can unite as one in immediately bearing witness to the great and miraculous change that will take place on our planet.

I. A PLANETARY EMERGENCY

THE TIME IS URGENT

"The hour is late; it's time to decide. I'm quite confident that you will make the choice wisely. In addressing global warming issues, the scientists have made it quite clear."[1]

—*Ban Ki-moon*

"We have a climate crisis that is a planetary emergency."

—Al Gore

The world's scientists fear that if we pass certain tipping points, the next stages of climate change would not only be fast but irreversible and catastrophic. So, there are already signs of this dangerous time approaching, through observations of lakes and elsewhere bubbling with methane gas that used to be stored safely below a frozen layer of the Earth.

No one knows when the day might be that enormous amounts are uncontrollably released, causing a sudden spike in temperature that could then catalyze runaway warming. That would be catastrophic for us.

Other devastating effects of climate change have already been occurring: The heat-reflecting Arctic ice is on its way to completely vanishing in a very near summer; rising sea levels and dozens of submerged or threatened islands; oceanic regions that are lifeless with dead zones are becoming too acidic to be livable due to excessive levels of CO_2; more frequent deadly wildfire; entire wildlife species going extinct 100 times faster than normal; more intense and destructive storms; disease-carrying mosquitoes spread by warming regions; disappearance of the world's glaciers; drying or disappeared lakes and rivers by the tens of thousands and the spreading of deserts.

As a consequence of these environmental impacts, two billion people are facing water shortages, and 20-million people are in a desperate state— like refugees except with no official protection.

These are truly almost always the consequences of humans' violent actions. The number one action is meat eating.

[In addition,] the livestock industry causes a large part of the world's soil erosion. It is a leading driver of desertification, biodiversity loss, and water waste, and water pollution, despite water becoming scarcer each day due to global warming. Moreover, the livestock sector inefficiently drains our fossil-fuel and food-grain resources. In short, we throw away 12 times more grain, at least 10 times more water and eight times more fossil-fuel energy to produce a portion of beef compared to a nutritionally similar or even greater amount of vegan food.

LIVESTOCK: THE MAJOR CAUSE OF THE GLOBAL CRISIS

The only way to avoid the "point of no return" climate catastrophe is to take action on the most climatically disastrous course of all—that is, meat production. By now we have all the evidence, all the information to safely say so. **The livestock industry is the top greenhouse gas generator.**

The last published findings from the United Nations in 2006 told us that the livestock industry causes greenhouse gas emissions more than all the world's transportation sectors combined —airplanes, trains, cars, motorcycles, etc., altogether.[2] **Updated calculations tell us that the livestock industry is responsible for at least 50% of global warming.**[3]

> "Our analysis shows that livestock and their byproducts actually account for at least 32,564-million tons of CO_2 per year, or 51 percent of annual worldwide GHG emissions."[4]
>
> —*Worldwatch Institute*

METHANE IS MORE POWERFUL THAN CO_2

Livestock is the primary human-caused emitter of methane, and methane not only has 72 times the heat-trapping ability, it is a shorter-lived gas. This means that it will leave the atmosphere much faster than CO_2, within just a decade as opposed to thousands of years for CO_2. Therefore, eliminating methane by eliminating livestock breeding is the fastest way to cool the planet.

Yes, we have to tackle the most important of emitters.

I pray all wise leaders will halt the lethal meat practice, which is the main force driving us to the point of no return right now. Otherwise, all other efforts to de-carbonize our economies may be cancelled out, or never have a chance to materialize in the first place.

We will destroy the world if we do not stop eating and producing meat and other animal products.

II. Our Food Choices are a Life-and-Death Issue

We are Devouring the Planet

If meat eating is not banned or not limited, then the whole planet will be gone. This is a life-and-death matter for everybody; it's not a personal choice. And we are eating meat, eating up the whole planet, eating up 90% of the food supply and letting other people hungry.[5] It's not a necessary choice at all.

Even before the planetary urgency, meat-eating people ate up the whole planet, ate up so much food and resulted in hunger and war, and it has never been a right choice in the first place.

> "Unless we change our food choices, nothing else matters because it is meat that is destroying most of our forests. It is meat that pollutes the waters. It is meat that is creating diseases, which leads to all our money being diverted to hospitals. So it's a first choice for anybody who wants to save the Earth."[6]
>
> —Maneka Gandhi

All these [global warming] situations are getting worse and worse and won't stop until we really change the way we live our life. The solution is quite easy: simply stop eating meat; that is the best solution. This is imperative now because of the perilous state of our planet and our limited time.

Stopping meat production will lower greenhouse gas emissions in the fastest possible way and halt the unspeakable environmental damage, ranging from climate change to land and water misuse, pollution, loss of wildlife and threats to human health.

Besides stopping 50% [of global warming]—I mean even more than that, this is just a very conservative estimate—there are many more other crucial benefits. It solves our water scarcity problem, our world hunger crisis, and land degradation and pollution problem.

If you compare [it] to a vegan diet, a meat diet uses up to 17 times as much land, 14 times as much water and 10 times as much energy.[7] We produce enough cereals to feed the entire human population over, abundantly. Yet, one-billion people are hungry, and 6-million young children die every year—that's one child dying every five seconds while we have abundance of food to feed all the world population and more, two times over even.[8] On the other hand, about one-billion people suffer from obesity and related diseases, from eating too much or too much meat.

So there are many, many practical reasons to be veg, aside from the compassionate nature that is cultivated by preserving all life. This is important, too. But if people just start with the vegan diet, the care for all life will also come by the way.

UN urges global move to a meat and dairy-free diet:

"Impacts from agriculture are expected to increase substantially due to the population growth increasing consumption of animals products. A substantial reduction of impacts would only be possible with a substantial worldwide diet change away from animal products."[9]

THE PLANT-BASED DIET IS THE QUICKEST SOLUTION

"Action to replace livestock products not only can achieve quick reductions in atmospheric GHGs, but can also reverse the ongoing world food and water crises."[10]

—*Worldwatch Institute*

Being vegan will have the immediate effect of removing methane from the atmosphere, which is one of the highest heat-retaining greenhouse gases, up to 72 times the heat-trapping effect of carbon dioxide.[11] Being vegan will surely slow down desertification and preserve your natural resources, like lakes and rivers, and protect your forests.

You can also employ other green measures, such as planting trees or changing to green technology, but those take longer to have an effect. The vegetarian diet is the fastest and also reduces the bad karma of killing, and thus, is the most important.

We conserve 70% clean water, save up to 70% of the Amazon rainforest from clearance for animal grazing.[12] And it would free up to 3.5-million hectares of land annually. It frees up to 760-million tons of grain every year—half of the world's grain supply, can you imagine that?[13] Consume 2/3 less fossil fuel than those used for meat production, reduce pollution from untreated animal waste, maintain clean air, save 4.5 tons of emissions per US household per year. And it will stop 80% global warming.[14]

Just talking about financial saving alone, scientists in the Netherlands found that of the estimated US$40 trillion needed to stop global warming, a full 80% of this amount would be saved with the vegan diet! That's a saving of US$32 trillion for the simple step of turning away from the meat to eating plant-based goods.[15]

The Earth has a mechanism to repair herself. It's just that we overload the planet. We pollute too much and we create too much of murderous karma. Therefore, the Earth is not even allowed to repair herself because of the bad karma of the inhabitants. As soon as we erase this bad retribution from the killing effect, then the Earth will turn around, will be allowed to repair, reproduce and sustain life again. It's all come around about the bad karma. We overload her capacity, the Earth, so we have to reverse our actions. That's all there is to it.

Then we will save the Earth, save our lives, and the lives of our children and animals as well. The Earth will become a paradise. Nobody will ever lack anything. No one will go hungry. No war, no disease, no disasters, no global warming, nothing anymore except peace, happiness and abundance. I promise in the name of the Buddha; it is like that.

KILLING ANIMALS BRINGS BAD KARMA

"As you sow, so shall you reap." "Like attracts like." Scientifically speaking, spiritually speaking, we have been warned. So, all the disasters that have happened around the world, of course, are connected with the human unkindness to the co-inhabitants. That was the price we have to pay for what we have done to the innocents who have done us no harm, who are also the children of God, who have been sent to Earth to help us and to cheer our days.

It's not the technical problem; it's not the technical reparation we have to concentrate on. It's the retribution, the cause and retribution that we have to pay attention to. The cost of killing, the cost of violence is far worse than any car, any sun's explosion or any ocean explosion combined together, because we have to be responsible for our actions. Every action provokes a counter reaction. So, we just have to stop killing. We just have to stop killing animals and man.

We have to stop it. And then everything else will suddenly become clear.

We will find better technical means to tackle the climate problem. The sunspots might even stop exploding. The ocean explosions might just stop. The typhoons might just stop. The cyclones will be silent. The earthquakes will just be gone. Everything else will turn to a peaceful way of life because we create peace and then we will have peace, peace not only among humans but among all co-inhabitants. That's why I keep emphasizing the vegetarian diet. It's the moral code of being a human. It is the mark of a great human.

COMPASSIONATE ENERGY CAN CHANGE EVERYTHING

Now the vegetarian diet is benevolent, so it will bring you happy energy and that in turn will breed more happiness, will attract more happiness and when you're happy everything will be better. You think better; you react better; your life becomes better. Your children will be better; everything will be better.

And the powerful collective, positive and loving power of the whole world will repel darkness that is coming towards us, that is facing us right now. That's the only solution I have.

You see, we have the energy to change everything, we have the power to dictate what happens around us, but we must use it. We must use it for the sake of all. We must use it for the benefit of every being on this planet. Our thinking, our action, has to send out a message to the universal energy that we want a better planet, we want a safer life, we want a saved world. Then the universal energy will do just that.

But we have to act in resonance with this energy, you see? If we want good things then we have to do good. If we want life, we have to spare lives. So the good energy we create can do these things, and more wonders. The compassionate, loving atmosphere that we, as the whole world, generate, can and will do more miracles for us.

We create everything that we want if we live but in accordance with the law of the universe. Such is the power of just being vegan. Because that means we spare life, we want life, we want constructive energy, we don't want destruction. So vegan is the answer.

The more spiritually elevated humankind is, then of course, the more global warming will lessen. When humankind becomes more spiritually uplifted and has more love for all people, for all beings, all situations, and all their environments, then global warming will be reduced day by day and will disappear completely. And after that, everyone in the world will live in peace, happiness, and will love one another. But everyone must wake up.

> I'm positive that our Earth will reach a higher level of consciousness and miracles will happen under Heaven's mercy.

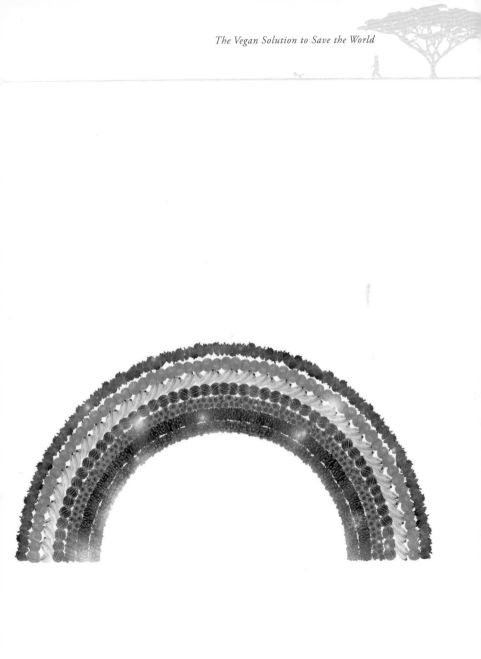

2

WARNING SIGNS TO AWAKEN HUMANITY

> Because of the critical state of the planet, if we don't act
> quickly there may be nothing left at all for us to even
> want to protect. At that time it might be too late. We
> cannot continue the trend like this forever and stop
> whenever [if] we want to save the planet. I'm sorry to
> say we have a limited time.

I. IT IS WORSE THAN THE WORST-CASE SCENARIO

Our current course of climate change is worse than the worst case scenario projected by the United Nations Intergovernmental Panel on Climate Change (IPCC), with the damaging and often fatal effects already being seen through such extreme events as hurricanes, flooding, droughts and heat waves.

Even if the world reduces greenhouse gas emissions, the planet will take time to recover from the gases already in the atmosphere.

This is why it is necessary to focus on short-lived gases, namely methane. Methane traps at least 72 times more heat than CO_2, averaged over a 20-year period. Methane's biggest source is the livestock industry, which is indeed one of the top causes of global warming that must be stopped.

But first, please allow me to share just some of the latest evidence of the impacts of climate change on humans' and animals' lives.

ARCTIC AND ANTARCTIC ICE MELTS

Arctic Meltdown

The Arctic, or North Pole, may be ice-free by 2012, 70 years ahead of IPCC estimations. Without the protective ice to reflect sunlight, 90 percent of the sun's heat can enter the open water, thus accelerating global warming.[16]

The change in Arctic ice cover is dramatic, with the climatologists saying that only 10 percent now is older and thick ice, while over 90 percent is newly formed and thin.[17]

The "Feedback Loop" and Runaway Global Warming

If the seawater is warmer, then the ice will be melted quicker. And once the ice has melted, there's no reflection of the heat back into space. Therefore, the heat will melt the ice as well and warm the water further. And both will help each other to melt more ice and heat up more the planet. You see the devil's cycle.

That's why the scientists could not predict it very well before, but they are very vigilant right now. They're keeping a good eye on the situation. It's just that we don't do things fast enough.[18]

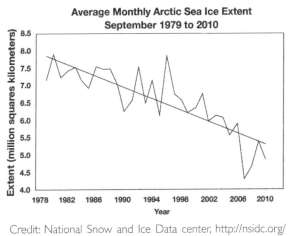

Credit: National Snow and Ice Data center, http://nsidc.org/
arcticseaicenews/index.html

Greenland and the Antarctic Ice Melts

As the massive ice sheets of Greenland and the Antarctic continue to melt as well, catastrophic sea-level rise and stronger storms are expected to follow. If the entire West Antarctic sheet melts, global average sea levels would rise at least by 3.3, 3.5 meters (10.8—11.8 feet),[19] affecting over 3.2 billion people—that is half of the world population—who live within 200 miles of coastlines.

The US scientists from the National Snow and Ice Data Center now say that if all of Antarctica were to melt, the sea level could rise to a much higher level than expected, some say even up to 70 meters (230 feet), which means more deadly to all lives on Earth.[20]

• Sinking Land and Climate Refugees

Due to rising sea levels, islands are sinking as we speak, with Tuvalu, Tonga and some 40 other island nations having to plan their whole country's migration.

A report from the International Organization for Migration stated that there may be 200-million, or even up to one-billion people who will be climate refugees by 2050, or within our lifetime.[21] These are people who must leave their island or coastal homes due to rising sea levels or permafrost melts that cause entire communities or nations to sink and collapse.[22]

(Please see Appendix 1 for data on sea level rise and its world-wide effects.)

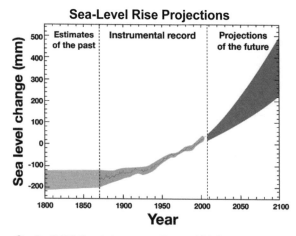

Credit: IPCC, *Fourth Assessment Report*, I I I, figure I.

Methane Hydrate: a Ticking Time Bomb

Another Arctic change is the thawing of permafrost, a normally frozen layer of earth containing methane stores [methane hydrate]. The thawing of this layer in recent years has caused methane to be released, with atmospheric levels that have risen sharply since 2004.[23]

Further global warming beyond a two-degree Celsius rise could cause billions of tons more of methane [hydrate from the bottom of the ocean] to be released into the atmosphere, leading to mass extinctions of life on this planet.

> "A temperature increase of merely a few degrees would cause these gases to volatilize and 'burp' into the atmosphere, which would further raise temperatures, which would release yet more methane, heating the Earth and seas further, and so on. There's 400 gigatons of methane locked in the frozen arctic tundra-enough to start this chain reaction… Once triggered, this cycle could result in runaway global warming."[24]
>
> —*Geologist John Atcheson*

It's not only the water rising that we are worried about; it's the gas, the hydrogen sulfide, and the methane, and all kinds of gases in the ocean.[25] And also it will melt more ice if the methane is coming out from the permafrost, etc., and from the ocean as well and from all the livestock, animal raising. It keeps adding together, and it would stay in the atmosphere for a long time.

At the point of no return that would be rolling downhill then; no change can be taken place anymore. Nothing can help anymore at that time. And there may be nobody who survives, or maybe very little.

Once the planet is destroyed, it will look like Mars, un-inhabitable. And it takes millions of years, sometimes hundreds of millions of years until any planet recovers, if it recovers at all.

The quicker we change, the better, and then we can halt
the climate change. And we can restore the planet very
quickly, in no time, but if we don't, then the planet will
also be destroyed quickly and in no time.

GLACIAL RETREAT AND WATER SHORTAGES

Effects of Glacial Retreat

Most of the planet's glaciers will be gone within a few decades,
jeopardizing the survival of more than two billion people. One billion of
these people will suffer the effects of the Himalayan glacier retreats, which
have been occurring at a pace more rapid than anywhere in the world, with
two-thirds of the region's more than 18,000 glaciers receding. [26] The initial
effects of glacier melt are destructive floods and landslides. As the glacial ice
retreat continues, reduced rainfall, devastating droughts and water shortages
are the result.[27]

The Dire Condition of the World's Glaciers

In the state of Montana, [U.S.A.], the famous glaciers of Glacier National
Park are now expected to disappear within a decade.[28] The Colorado River
[which relies on snow pack,] which supplies water to seven Western states,
is going dry.[29]

Peru is home to 70% of the entire range of Andean glaciers, with
peaks that supply the country's people with both water and hydroelectric
power. These are all expected to disappear by 2015, just a few more years.[30]

Dwindling water supplies have caused escalating tensions and even conflicts to erupt as many people, including disadvantaged farmers, don't have enough water or are struggling for their share.

(Please see Appendix 2 for more information on global glacial retreat.)

OVERFISHING, DEAD ZONES AND OCEAN ACIDIFICATION

The US-based Pew Commission found that overfishing is the greatest threat to marine ecosystems, followed by agricultural runoff, including livestock manure and fertilizers used on animal feed crops.[31]

Climate change is creating areas of sea known as dead zones, which now number more than 400. These [dead zones] arise due to fertilizer runoff largely from livestock, contributing to the lack of oxygen which is necessary to support life.[32]

Waters polluted with red tide that causes dead zones at Copacabana beach, Rio de Janeiro, Brazil.

Scientists estimate that more than 90% of the oceans' big fish have disappeared over the last 50 years due to commercial fishing.[33]

They warned that at the present rate of fishing, there will be a global collapse of all species being fished by 2050 and say that recovery efforts need to be started immediately.[34]

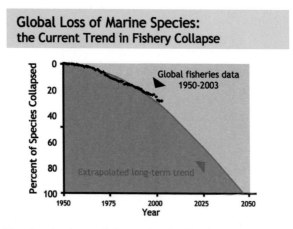

Global Loss of Marine Species:
the Current Trend in Fishery Collapse

"Accelerating Loss of Ocean Species Threatens Human Well-being," Science, November 3, 2006, http:// www.compassonline. org/pdf_files/WormEtAlSciencePR.pdf and B. Worm et al., "Impacts of Biodiversity Loss on Ocean Ecosystem Services."

The lack of certain fish has contributed to higher ocean acidity, which in turn, reduces the capacity of the ocean to absorb CO_2.

The whales and dolphins are thus being driven from the ocean as conditions worsen; it is suffocating them. Sometimes hundreds at a time, they're dying on the beach because they cannot tolerate this toxic condition in the seawater anymore.[35]

EXTREME WEATHER CONDITIONS

The past decade has twice, at least, seen the hottest average annual temperatures ever recorded in our planet's history. In 2003, a record heat wave hit Europe, claiming tens of thousands of lives. Heat waves also preceded the worst wildfires ever in Australia's history.[36]

Puebla State [in Mexico] has seen increased forest fires over the past few years; rainfall decreased by 200 liters per square meter; [there has been an] increase in average annual temperatures to 17.5 degrees Celsius. The winter temperatures are now also above normal.

In the past five years [2003-2007], Peru had at least three extreme temperature events and floods affecting more than 500,000 people. Within just 30 years, floods increased by more than 60%, and mudflows increased by 400%.[37] [Peruvian] President Garcia declared a state of emergency in 2009 due to climate change-related, severe cold and freezing conditions in the southern Andes that caused the death of nearly 250 children, and sickened many others.[38]

(Please see Appendix 3 for updated data on extreme global weather conditions.)

> "Climate is defined not simply as average temperature and precipitation but also by the type, frequency and intensity of weather events. Human-induced climate change has the potential to alter the prevalence and severity of extremes such as heat waves, cold waves, storms, floods and droughts."[39]
>
> —The United States Environmental Protection Agency

INCREASED FREQUENCY OF NATURAL DISASTERS

Drought, Desertification and Wildfires

According to the United Nations, desertification, which often results from felling too many trees and damage that occurs from such activities as cattle grazing, is affecting the well-being of more than 1.2-billion people in more than 100 countries at risk.[40]

Precious fresh water supplies are also drying up, such as aquifers under the major cities of Beijing, Delhi, Bangkok and dozens of other regions such as the Midwestern United States, while the Rivers Ganges, Jordan, Nile and Yangtze have been reduced to a trickle for much of the year.

In China's worst drought in five decades [in 2009], vital crops were lost in at least 12 northern provinces, costing the nation billions of US dollars in drought relief to farmers with losses.[41]

In 2009, in Nepal and Australia, wildfires were severely intensified by drought conditions.[42] In Africa, people in Somalia, Ethiopia and Sudan, to name just a few, have been crippled by drought.

Researchers say that the US West is facing a devastating drought crisis as snows from mountains are releasing vast reservoirs of water.

(Please see Appendix 4 for information on major global drought and wildfire disasters.)

Increasing Frequency of Storms and Floods

The intensity and duration of hurricanes and tropical storms have been noted to increase by 100% over the past 30 years, which scientists at the Massachusetts Institute of Technology (MIT) in the United States say is likely due to climate-related increases in ocean temperature.

According to researchers at Georgia Institute of Technology, U.S.A., worldwide the number of the most destructive Category 4 and 5 hurricanes has doubled over the past 35 years. Category 5 storms yield the highest level of destruction in major cities. Their intensity and duration have also increased by 75% since the 1970s.

One of these storms, whose effects can still be seen and felt, was the 2005 Hurricane Katrina, which devastated, especially, areas of New Orleans, with people who are still recovering their homes and their lives today.

The US National Oceanic and Atmospheric Administration said that for the first time on record, in 2008 six consecutive tropical cyclones made landfall on the United States' mainland.

The North Atlantic Ocean and the Indian Ocean are the two areas with the strongest hurricane trends.

(Please see Appendix 5 for data on major global flood disasters.)

Supreme Master Ching Hai International Association's relief work in Pakistan, 2010

Supreme Master Ching Hai International Association's relief work in Haiti, 2010

Earthquakes

Scientists have discovered that earthquakes are linked to global warming because as the ice melts at the poles and beneath Greenland, pressure shifts on the Earth's plates that could trigger movement to cause earthquakes.

One of the most tragic disasters of our time was the tsunami [resulting from an earthquake] that struck [Indonesia] in 2004 that brought so much sorrow for the Indonesian people and the people of the world.

(Please see Appendix 6 for updated data on global earthquake disasters.)

Insect Infestation

In the United States, close to a million acres of pine forest have been lost in the Rocky Mountains due to beetle infestation from global warming. Similar [situations are] also in Canada.

DEFORESTATION

> The rainforest is the lung of our planet. As the trees are felled and plants become more exposed and dry, they even emit carbon dioxide rather than absorb it. This is another danger that is attacking us.

In Brazil, 90% of the land deforested since 1970 has gone toward livestock pasture or feed.[43] **Lush forests are being turned into barren fields at a rate of 36 football fields per minute, are being destroyed as we are speaking.**[44]

And in the southern part of Mexico, tropical forests that once covered almost half of the State of Tabasco have been reduced to less than 10% their original size. At the same time, pastureland for livestock has increased to 60% of the State's total area.[45]

Also, in countries like Argentina and Paraguay, more and more forests are felled for both livestock and soy crops. Argentina has lost 70% of her original forests.[46]

Indonesia has the world's third biggest rainforest, only behind the Amazon and the Congo. Yet, [Indonesian] rainforest is being lost at an alarming rate of one football field per minute. The United Nations says that 98% of the whole forest could be gone in just 15 years.[47]

The Amazon rainforest alone contains more carbon dioxide than 10 years worth of all human-produced greenhouse gases. Plus, when we burn the forests, we release black carbon, which are particles of soot that trap 680 times the heat of the same amount of CO_2.[48]

LOSS OF BIODIVERSITY

Leading ecologists say that the decline of wildlife due to species extinction is so rapid that there is no modern comparison. Scientists also now predict that the Earth's 16,000 endangered species may become extinct 100 times faster than previously thought.

"Eminent Harvard biologist Edward O Wilson, and other scientists, estimate that the true rate of extinction is more like 1,000 to 10,000 times the background rate. **Between 2.7 and 270 species are erased from existence each day.**"[49]

—*Julia Whitty*

"20%-40% of the species of organisms on Earth are likely to go extinct during the present century on the basis of global warming alone, without even the other factors coming into it."[50]

—*The Intergovernmental Panel on Climate Change*

WATER SHORTAGE

Dwindling water supplies have caused escalating tensions and even conflicts to erupt as many people, including disadvantaged farmers, don't have enough water or are struggling for their share.

There're tens of thousands of rivers and lakes dying all over the world. People are dying from droughts. People are leaving their villages, their hometowns because they don't have any more water to drink.[51]

One billion people have no access to clean, safe water. And 1.8-million children die every year due to sickness from contaminated water.[52]

FOOD SHORTAGE

The United Nations announced that as of 2009 the world is now seeing the highest number of hungry people in four decades. There are 1.02-billion people with not enough food in the world.[53]

In Peru, due to excessive heat and droughts over the last 12 years, 140,000 hectares of potatoes and corn have been ruined—equal to food that could have fed 11-million people.

[In Africa,] Zimbabwe, Somalia, Mauritius, Mozambique and Sudan—just to name a few—are experiencing worsened droughts that make it difficult to plant crops, thus adding to food shortages and prices rising.

Add to this desertification and deforestation that further degrade the land. Increased temperatures mean erratic rainfall—either too little or too much at a time—so we have ravaging floods that drown the crops and fires that burn the forest.

These impacts of climate change increase food insecurity and the food crisis.

(Please see Appendix 7 for data on climate change and the worldwide food shortage.)

HUMAN HEALTH

People Suffering from Climate Change

According to Swiss-based research, climate change is already responsible for some 315,000 deaths a year, with another 325-million people who are severely affected.[54] This comes in addition to an economic loss of US$125 billion every year.[55] The worst affected are developing nations in Africa, with other very threatened areas being in South Asia and small island nations.

Furthermore, 99% of the people who lose their lives due to natural disasters are in Asia.

Diseases Spread by Insects

Mosquitoes causing dengue fever are being seen for the first time in Piura [Peru], as they spread to new areas due to climate change.[56]

There is also increased risk of diseases such as malaria because the mosquitoes spread to higher altitudes. The United Nations is afraid that hundreds of millions of people in Africa are at risk.[57]

(Please see Appendix 8 for an excerpt from *Six Degrees: Our Future on a Hotter Planet* by Mark Lynus.)

II. We Are Running out of Time

According to all the scientific evidence and all the physical evidence up to date, we don't have much time. Even later on, if we want to save the planet, it won't be successful.

The threats imposed by global warming are more than imminent; they are already here, as you can see through many disasters, upheavals, climate refugees, phenomena around the world.

According to expert scientists, the atmospheric temperatures are rising so steeply that we do not have much time left to change.

> "We have passed tipping points. We have not passed a point of no return. We can still roll things back, but it is going to require a quick turn in direction."[58]
>
> —Dr. James Hansen, Head of the NASA Goddard Institute for Space Studies

So many world leaders and scientists are also worrying about this. The truth is, we are already not able to handle such situations in places where global warming is already reaching extreme degrees.

Some countries and communities have to cope with worsened drought situations. There is not enough water to raise crops or even to drink. Their rivers and lakes are drying up or completely gone. Glaciers melt in many places so dramatically that one moment there are massive floods, and soon after, a drought.

So how can we handle the mass migration of tens of millions of people all at once due to desertification, the rising sea levels or the permanent loss of crop fields? It's very difficult and maybe even impossible.

We are not ready at all. We are not prepared enough.

We have to save this planet, so that we'll be able to stay, first. Because if the ice all melts, if all the poles all melt out, and then if the sea is warm, then the gas might be released from the ocean, and we might all be poisoned. It's a lot of gas.

If you see the Singapore lecture [Sept, 1994], I already warned that we have to change the way we live; otherwise it's too late. It was 10 or 15 years [ago]. Or before that, I always talked about how we deforest our planet, meat eating and all that contributes to a lot of damage to our Earth planet.

Scientists say many things. They are listening now, but I just hope they do it fast. It just takes action. All the governments in the world really take it now seriously. It's just I'm worried the action might be too slow, that's all. Because the ice is reflecting the sun and sends it back into the space, but the ice is melting so fast now that there's not enough reflection and because the sea is already warm, it melts the ice. And because the ice melts, the sea is warmer. You see what I mean, the cycle?

The way it is going, if they don't fix it, [in] four or five years' time, finito. No more. It's really that urgent.

III. Tackle the Root Problem Now

Stop the Greatest Contributor to Our Environmental Crisis

> "Livestock are one of the most significant contributors to today's most serious environmental problems. Urgent action is required to remedy the situation." [59]

—Dr. Henning Steinfeld, Chief of Livestock Information and Policy Branch, FAO, UN.

> "Livestock is the main driver of deforestation. Livestock is the largest single source of water pollution. Livestock produces more greenhouse gases than all worldwide transportation combined."

—*Livestock's Long Shadow*

Stop blaming the CO_2 for every problem of global warming on our planet. We are to be blamed. The meat industry is to be blamed. The meat industry is the one we have to focus on to stop, to abolish. To stop the climate change and to stop the waste of the forests and land, stop talking around the subject. Talk to the point: Meat industry must stop.

The smartest way would be to stop the worsening of global warming by being vegan. It sounds very simple but it is the best solution, the most effective, and the effect of it will be felt almost immediately. Without this main, most time-effective change, no matter what we try to do, it won't be enough to repel the worst consequences that we have accumulated.

Moreover, the problems we already face now—such as the warming atmosphere, water shortage, food scarcity, and desertification—we can quickly eliminate by stopping meat production. Stop it now, no further!

> "Don't eat meat. This is something that the IPCC was afraid to say earlier, but now we have said it: Please eat less meat—meat is a very carbon intensive commodity." [60]

—Dr. Rajendra K. Pachauri

The Root Problem is a Spiritual One

"Nothing will benefit human health and increase chances for survival of life on Earth as much as the evolution to a vegetarian diet." [61]

—*Albert Einstein*

As I have mentioned before, we have to tackle the root of the problem. The root of the problem is the cause of global warming, and that root is our unkindness to our co-inhabitants.

Every action provokes a reaction, and this is very scientific.

You see, if we sow an apple seed, we will get an apple tree and from that apple tree, after a while it will bear apple fruits for us. This is a circle of life. If we kill, we cannot expect life from it. Every action bears the same fruits afterwards. It's not religious speaking; it is scientific.

So, now, the root of our problem is that we have been unkind to our co-inhabitants: the living, feeling, walking, acting, loving beings, like animals, of all size and shapes. And we have also been unkind to our environment. So, we have been massacring our co-inhabitant animals, and we have been destroying our environment, like deforesting and destroying the water and destroying the air. From all this, we cannot expect a better outcome.

These mournful cries, the utter misery and pain of these suffering animals that live in filth, oppressed, in the torturous confines of tight cages, and live in darkness every day, never seeing the sunlight again, and also the extreme agony before and after being killed, have shaken Heaven and Earth.

Therefore, the natural disasters, droughts are to wash away the evil deeds of humankind and serve as a warning, as well as to advise humans to change for the better so that the future would be bright, happy, and there won't be suffering, similar to that of the animals.

"What you sow, so shall you reap." Any holy book teaches us to be like that, so humankind needs to wake up; otherwise, we will have to bear the consequences.

So, in order to solve the problem that we are facing right now, we have to reverse our actions. We have to be kind to our co-inhabitants. Instead of killing them, massacring them, sacrificing them, we have to take care of them, have to be kind to them, look after them. And instead of deforestation, we have to plant trees again. Take care of whatever environment that we have. And instead of polluting our planet, the air, we have to turn to friendly energy and sustainable energy. Just reverse our actions.

We should be in coordination with the universal energy, the loving law of nature. If humanity does not respect other forms of life, then the life of humans will also be in peril, because we are all interconnected.

We all depend on each other to survive, down to the little worm that makes our land arable. But if people turn away from killing, and choose the animal-free lifestyle, they will harvest from the seeds of peace and kindness.

We pray that enough people do so, and quickly, as we are running out of time.

RETURN TO OUR LOVING SELVES AND SAVE THE PLANET

We must understand that natural disasters are the consequence of the negative energy in our atmosphere. And this negative energy in our atmosphere is created by our feelings, our thoughts, and actions of either hatred, violence, and of killing so many humans' and innocent animals' lives. If we don't change our disaster-breeding, provoking way, then disasters will never end.

We must change our pattern of thinking and lifestyle to a higher and more compassionate and nobler level. We must return to our true, loving selves by cherishing and protecting all lives, starting with an immediate vegan diet to save our planet, which is precious and beautiful. Vegan, vegetarian is the best and fastest solution.

Being veg is beneficial for any kind of spiritual advancement. In fact, all the wise, ancient teachings of sages since time immemorial have highlighted the importance of a benevolent plant-based diet. It is a fundamental requirement of a spiritual practitioner.

The concept behind forgoing animal products is ahimsa—meaning nonviolence. By partaking of a vegan diet, we also avoid the bad retribution of killing and thus it will not burden and obstruct our spiritual journey.

Being vegan simply means that we protect all the animals. This killing of other beings must be stopped for humanity to evolve as a civilization. The benefits of doing so are manifold. Besides the restoration of health, biodiversity will be allowed to thrive, planet equilibrium restored, along with the easing of our own conscience and our capacity for elevated consciousness.

All these are the fruits of a more compassionate diet. This loving attitude also creates a more peaceful atmosphere that brings greater comfort to all beings. At peace with ourselves in the knowledge that we did not cause anguish or pain to our fellow animal brethren, we will have the inner tranquility to pursue our spiritual endeavors wholeheartedly.

And on a bigger scale, our planet will also be healed. Just like an individual being healed by turning to a compassionate diet—like attracts like. The good, loving, compassionate energy will ward off the darkness that is looming toward us, that is next to us right now.

We will, in short, have a paradise on Earth.

PLEASE WAKE UP!

by Supreme Master Ching Hai

O, world, wake up and behold
Rivers and mountains are in tumult
Burnt forests, eroded hills, desiccated streams
Whither do the poor souls go in the end?

O, great Earth, lessened be your agony
For these tears to wane with the persistent night.
O, seas and lakes, cease not your melodies
Allowing hope for a morrow among humanity...

O, sentient beings, have respite in the realm beyond
Though you departed without any utterance.
Let the throbbing of my heart abate
While I await Earthlings' timely repentance.

O, deep forests, preserve your true selves
Protect the human race in their moments of erring.
Please accept my heartfelt thousand teardrops
To nurture your majestic trees, leaves and roots.

O, heart, relent your sobbing
For my soul to rest in long nights.
Tears dried up and I'm wordless
Weeping in sympathy for the tormented!

O, night, please kindle your source of light
Shine the way for those human souls in darkness
Be serene for my mind to still
And enter emptiness with the miraculous celestial melody.

O, day, stir not sudden unrests
For peace to repose in our very hearts
For humankind's struggles to subside
For the true Self to gloriously shine!

O, heart of mine, lament no longer
Like an insect writhing in the chilling winter.
Calmly wait for a perfect tomorrow
And the day the world turns into Paradise.

O, I cry, I plead, I pray, I beg!
O, infinite Buddhas,
Bodhisattvas, angels
Deliver souls straying from the True Path
Wandering in the endless cycle of suffering migration.

O, brother, wake up at once!
Proudly walk on great seas and rivers
Look straight at the flaming sun
And vow sacrifice to save all beings.

O, sister, wake up this instant!
Arise from places of devastation
Together let's renew our planet
For all to sing joyous songs of oneness.

3

ORGANIC VEGANISM TO HEAL THE PLANET

Veganism will save our world. Adopting a plant-based diet can halt as much as 80% of global warming, eradicate world hunger, stop war, promote peace, and it will free up the Earth's water as well as many other precious resources, offering a lifeline for the planet and for humanity. In short, it will very quickly halt many of the global problems facing us right now.

Many of these areas where we are seeing such devastating effects of climate change, such as Arctic melt, lands sinking, water shortage from glacier melt and even storms increasing are all directly related to the Earth's temperature increasing. So, we must cool the planet, first and foremost. And the best way to stop global warming is to stop producing the greenhouse gases that create the heat.

We already know about the efforts to reduce emissions such as from industry and transportation. But changes in these sectors are taking too much time—more than we can afford at this rate, at this hour. **One of the most effective and fastest ways to reduce the heat in the atmosphere is to eliminate methane production.**

Methane not only traps up to 72 times more heat than carbon, it also goes away from the atmosphere much faster than CO_2. So if we stop producing methane, the atmosphere will cool more quickly than if we stop producing carbon dioxide.

Organic vegan will produce a beneficial, cooling effect as it will cut down methane and other greenhouse gases which are fatal to our survival.

Organic, because we don't want harmful chemicals to be sprayed everywhere, and running into our water, poisoning the river, the soil and all living things, making humans sick as well. Also organic because this practice will absorb huge amounts of CO_2 already existing in the air, thus cooling our planet.

I. COOL THE PLANET AND RESTORE THE ENVIRONMENT

ELIMINATE METHANE, BLACK CARBON AND OTHER GREENHOUSE GASES

Livestock—the Greatest Methane Emitter

Carbon dioxide is not our worst threat; methane is. And methane comes from livestock raising.

We can start by cutting down on the biggest methane producer in the world; that is, animal raising. So, to cool the planet most quickly, we have to stop consuming meat in order to stop the livestock-raising industry, and thus stop greenhouse gases, methane and other toxic gases from the animal industry.

Greenhouse Gases and Global Warming Potentials

Greenhouse gases	CO_2 (carbon dioxide)	CH_4 (methane)	N_2O (nitrous oxide)
Global Warming Potentials (GWP)*	1	25*	298*
Pre-industrial atmospheric concentration	280 ppm	0.715 ppm	0.270 ppm
Atmospheric concentration in 2005	379 ppm	1.774 ppm	0.319 ppm
Percentile contribution from livestock industry**	9%	37%	65%

* Averaged over 100 years, methane and nitrous oxide are 25 and 298 times respectively more potent than carbon dioxide in global warming potentials. Averaged over 20 years, methane is 72 times more potent. (One part per million (ppm) denotes one part per 1,000,000 parts.) (IPCC, *Fourth Assessment Report*, 2007, Table 2.14)

** Steinfeld et al., *Livestock's Long Shadow*, 2006

If everyone in the world would adopt this simple but most powerful practice of an animal-free diet, then we could reverse the effect of global warming in no time. We would then have time to actually be able to adopt longer-term measures such as more green technology to also remove the carbon dioxide from the atmosphere.

In fact, if we neglect to stop meat production, either all these green efforts will be cancelled out in effect, or we may lose the planet before we are even having a chance to install any green technology such as the wind power or solar power or more hybrid cars, for that reason.

Researchers from NASA just announced that methane, the potent greenhouse gas whose largest human-created source is the livestock industry, traps a hundred times more heat than carbon dioxide over a five-year period.

"Methane heats the Earth 72 times more than
CO_2 in 20 years of time." [62]

—Intergovernmental Panel on Climate Change

"Methane heats the Earth 100 times more than
CO_2 in five years of time."
"A ton of methane emitted today will exert more
warming in one year than a ton of CO_2 emitted
today would exert until 2075."[63]

—Dr Kirk Smith, Professor of Global Environmental Health, University of California, Berkeley

Please also keep in mind that although livestock has been reported to generate 18% of global greenhouse gas emissions, which is more than the world's transportation sectors combined, this is actually an underestimate because recently revised calculations have placed it at generating possibly more than 50% of total global emissions. **I repeat: Livestock has been recalculated as to generate possibly more than 50% of total global emissions —more than 50% is from the livestock industry. So that was the number one solution.**[64]

The Danger of Methane Hydrate and Hydrogen Sulfide

When it's cold, [methane hydrate is] just compressed [under the ocean floor] and lies there, harmless. But now as the weather is getting warmer, these gases are going to be released. They are already releasing into the atmosphere, as you know from scientific reports. The permafrost layer is melting each day.[65]

There are already signs of this dangerous time approaching, through observations of lakes and elsewhere bubbling with methane gas that used to be stored safely below a frozen layer of the Earth.[66] No one knows when the day might be that enormous amounts are uncontrollably released, causing a sudden spike in temperature that could then catalyze runaway warming. That would be catastrophic for us.

"Permafrost is like a time bomb waiting to go off—as it continues to thaw, tens of thousands of teragrams of methane can be released into the atmosphere, enhancing climate warming. This newly recognized source of methane is so far not included in climate models."[67] (one teragram = one million tons)

—*Dr. Katey Walter, Aquatic Ecosystem Ecologist at the University of Alaska*

So, it's not just methane we are worried about. There are so many gases from the ocean. [For example,] hydrogen sulfide is credited with wiping out the 90% plus living creatures in our Earth's history in the past.[68]

Depending on the concentration dose, just the hydrogen sulphide alone can cause irritation of different body organs: eyes, nose, throat, bronchial constriction, spontaneous abortion, impaired bodily functions, headaches, dizziness, vomiting, coughing, difficult breathing, eye damage, shock, coma, death, etc.

We even might die from gas, not to talk about global warming yet. Right now, there's so much methane already released into the atmosphere many people have more mental illness or other physical suffering, according to scientists' research.

Methane gas can cause headaches, respiratory-system and heart malfunctions, and in more concentrated doses, death by suffocation. It is similar to carbon monoxide poisoning. It is 23 times more deadly than CO_2.

Other Lethal Gases from Livestock

Other lethal, toxic gases are emitted by the livestock industry as well. It is the largest source at 65% of global nitrous oxide, a greenhouse gas with approximately 300 times the warming potential of CO_2. It emits also 64% of all ammonia, which causes acid rain and hydrogen sulfide, a fatal gas. So to stop livestock production is to eliminate all these deadly gases, as well as methane.[69]

The Devastating Effects of Black Carbon

Black carbon is a greenhouse particle that is 680 times as heat-trapping as CO_2, and it causes the ice sheets and glaciers around the world to melt even faster. Up to 40% of black carbon emissions come from burning forests for livestock.

Scientists found that 60% of the black carbon particles in Antarctica were carried there by the wind from South American forests that are burned to clear land for livestock production.[70]

Stop Meat Production to Achieve a Rapid Cooling Effect

If we want to see the cooling of our planet in the next one or two decades, it's more effective to reduce methane first. And because the greatest source of methane on the planet is from livestock, to be a vegan is the fastest way to reduce methane, thus bringing cooling to the planet, successfully and fast.

U.S. researcher and IPCC member Dr. Kirk Smith has shown that within just a few years the dissipation rate of methane overtakes CO_2, and it's nearly completely gone within a decade, but CO_2 will stay around warming the planet for thousands of years! So, if we want a quicker cooling of the planet we have to eliminate those that leave the atmosphere quickly.[71]

In other words, methane does much more damage in the short run, but if we stop it, we will be able to reverse the trend of global warming very fast.

The best thing is stop eating meat, stop killing animals, stop raising animals. Then the methane gas and the nitrous oxide gas will stop! And then we cut already a big chunk of pollution off our air, and we cut off the global warming process. I said already, 80% of it will be cut almost immediately, and we can see the results in a few weeks.

PRESERVE THE OCEANS

Halt the Production of Dead Zones

There are other huge benefits gained by halting livestock production. Oceanic dead zones, for example, are caused primarily by fertilizer runoff from agriculture that is mainly used for animal feed.

Dead zones are a serious threat to the ocean's ecosystems, but they can be revived if we stop polluting them with our livestock-related activities.

The enormous dead zone in the Gulf of Mexico, the size of New Jersey, which suffocates all marine life there, is overwhelmingly due to the nitrogen runoff from the Midwest, from the animal wastes and the fertilizers for the animal feed crops. This waste is toxic. It contains antibiotics, hormones and pesticides, and 10 to 100 times the concentration of deadly pathogens like *E. coli* and salmonella compared to human waste.[72]

In 1995 one time, an eight-acre, large pig-manure lagoon burst in North Carolina, spilling 25-million gallons of this poisonous waste, twice the volume of the notorious Exxon-Valdez oil spill [260,000 to 750,000 barrels or 41,000 to 119,000 m³ of crude oil.] Hundreds of millions of fish in the state's New River were killed instantly due to the nitrates in the waste, with further harmful effects once the contamination reached the ocean.[73]

> "The number of oxygen-depleted, oceanic dead zones has
> increased from only 49 in the 1960s to 405 in 2008."[74]
>
> — *Robert J. Diaz and Rutger Rosenberg, Top Marine Ecologists*

Stop Fishing and Revive Marine Life

> We desperately need the fish in the sea to balance the ocean;
> otherwise, our lives will be in danger.

Fishing contributes to global warming primarily by disturbing the complex ecosystems of the world's oceans. Balanced marine ecosystems are extremely important, as more than two-thirds of the planet is covered by oceans.

The ocean is a very complex ecosystem where every living thing has a unique function. So, removing even a small fish for humans to eat creates an imbalance in the sea. In fact, we are already seeing an effect of this imbalance on marine mammals.

Stop fishing and then marine life will rebound. Since the heavy fishing that caused the sardines to disappear from the coast of Namibia, eruptions of harmful gases have created a dead zone that is destroying the area's ecosystems due to the absence of that one humble but eco-beneficial, powerful species.[75]

Overfishing has caused the remaining fish to be smaller, so the mesh size of the nets has been decreased to capture smaller fish, resulting in other fish being caught as well. So, it destroys even more marine ecosystems and destroys more fish life. These are either ground up as animal feed, used as fertilizer or thrown back into the ocean as dead fish. For example, for every one ton of prawns caught, three tons of other fish are also killed and thrown away.

Also, a US study revealed that pigs and chickens are forced to consume more than twice the seafood that is eaten by all the Japanese people, and six times the amount consumed by humans in the United States. At least one-third of all the world's fish caught today is fed to livestock, not to us humans even.

"If the various estimates we have received come true, then we are in the situation where 40 years down the line we, effectively, are out of fish." [76]

—Pavan Sukhdev, Head of the UN Environment
Program's Green Economy Initiative

There's another condition called acidification, where the lack of certain fish has contributed to higher ocean acidity, which in turn reduces the capacity of the ocean to absorb CO_2.

Fish farms are like on-land factory farms. They have similar problems environmentally, with impacts that include polluting the bodies of waters. The farmed fish are contained in big, netted areas off the ocean shores with uneaten food, fish waste, antibiotics or other drugs and chemicals that pass into the surrounding waters where they harm our ecosystems and pollute our drinking sources.

So, for anyone who thinks that eating fish does not cause as much environmental damage, please think again. Consuming any animal products at all negatively impacts our oceans and our world.

STOP WATER SHORTAGES

Livestock: the Greatest Water Guzzler

> "We must reconsider our agricultural practices and how we manage our water resources, with agriculture and livestock raising accounting for 70% of fresh water use and up to 80% of deforestation."
>
> —Ban Ki-moon

Water means everything to our existence. We must conserve the water; we must do everything we can. And the first step to begin is to be vegan, because the animal industry uses over 70% of the clean water of our planet.

While 1.1-billion people lack access to safe drinking water, we waste 3.8 trillion tons of precious clean water each year for livestock production.

We have [over] six-billion people in this world and the sources of groundwater for wells, which supports half of our world population, are dying, drying up. And the top ten global river systems are drying or ebbing away. And three-billion people are short of water.

Are we short of water?

One serving of BEEF uses over 1,200 gallons of water

One serving of CHICKEN uses 330 gallons of water

One Complete VEGAN meal with TOFU, RICE, and VEGETABLES uses only 98 gallons of water [77]

Even if we don't shower, we don't brush our teeth, it amounts to nothing when they don't stop eating meat.

The Americans already worry about the shortage of water. Their glacier has melted a lot. And the rivers have become drier. In a few more years only, the water might not be even enough for 23-million people who depend on that water to survive.[78]

The Organic Vegan Diet: Saving over 90% of the World's Water

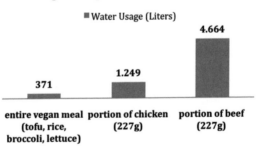

Be Organic Vegan to Save World's Water

■ Water Usage (Liters)

		4.664
	1.249	
371		
entire vegan meal (tofu, rice, broccoli, lettuce)	portion of chicken (227g)	portion of beef (227g)

Data Source: Marcia Kreith, *Water Inputs in California Food Production*, Water Education Foundation, September, 1991 (chart E3 p28)

Meat production uses massive amounts of water. It takes up to 1,200 gallons of fresh and good, clean water to produce just one serving of beef.[79] In contrast, a full vegan meal costs only 98 gallons of water. That is like 90-plus percent less.

We can stop water shortages. While droughts are plaguing more populations, we cannot afford to waste water. So, if we want to stop water shortages and to preserve precious water, we have to stop animal products.

PRESERVE THE LAND

Stop Overgrazing and Desertification

> The livestock sector is the single largest human use of land
> and the top driving force behind rainforest destruction.

We must stop livestock grazing to protect our soil and protect our life. Overgrazing by livestock is a major cause of desertification and other damage, and is responsible for more than 50% of land erosion.

We have only 30% of land that covers the Earth. Of that precious 30%, one-third of it is used, not for our true survival, but for livestock pasture or growing tons of grain for animal feed—all to produce a few pieces of meat.

For example, about one-billion acres or 80% of all agricultural land in the US, and about half of all US land are being used for meat production. By contrast, less than three-million acres is used to grow all the vegetables in the country.[80]

In Mexico, recent research stated that 47% of the land has already taken the toll of desertification due to damage from the cattle industry.[81] And another 50 to 70% of the county is suffering from some degree of drought.

The clearing of land for livestock has created instability and serious soil degradation across Mexico. In the northern regions of Mexico nearly two-thirds of the land is classified as being in a total or accelerated state of erosion.[82] When the livestock eats all the vegetation and tramples the land, what is left behind is cement-like ground, unable to grow anything. This worsens global warming because more carbon is released from the dying plants and bare soil.

ERADICATE WORLD HUNGER

> If everyone ate a plant-based diet, there would be
> enough food to satisfy 10-billion people.

Waste of Land for Raising Livestock

Are we short of food?
How many people in the world are hungry?
1.02-billion people
Every five seconds, a child dies of hunger.
Grain currently fed to livestock is enough to feed nearly two-billion people.[83]

—*Julie Gellatley and Tony Hardle*

Ninety percent of all soy, 80% of all corn and 70% of all grain grown in the United States are fed to fatten livestock, while this could feed at least 800-million hungry people.[84] We have hungry people; we have children dying every few seconds because we use too much land, too much water, too much food for livestock instead of on humans.

If we don't eat meat, we will use the agriculture products, cereals, to feed humans instead of feeding more bred animals in the future. So we don't have hunger anymore, and there will be no more war because of hunger. The effect is immense.

Land-Use Efficiency

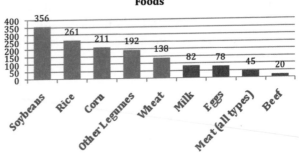

Pounds of Usable Protein Per Acre from Various Foods

Soybeans 356, Rice 261, Corn 211, Other Legumes 192, Wheat 138, Milk 82, Eggs 78, Meat (all types) 45, Beef 20

Date Source: USDA; FAO/WHO/UNICEF Protein Advisory Group, 2004

"It takes from six to 12 pounds of plant proteinto
produce one pound of flesh.
It takes about 1,000 times more water to produce
flesh than it does to produce potatoes or wheat.
It takes two hectares of land to support one omnivore.
It takes 1.2 hectares of land to support 20 vegans.

So it takes 80 times more land, basically, to
support the lifestyle of an omnivore than it does
the lifestyle of a vegan."[85]

—*Gary L. Francione, Professor of Law, Rutgers University Law School, USA, Vegan*

In addition, the more we use organic, natural farming methods, the
more food we have, the healthier we become and the healthier the soil will
become. And from then on, the soil will recover and then we will have more
and more abundance of food.

STOP DEFORESTATION

We have to ban deforestation, and we have to plant more trees, of course.
Wherever there's erosion or empty land we have to plant trees.

Deforestation is also largely driven by meat production. With the
United Nations estimating that deforestation accounts for approximately
20% of all greenhouse gas emissions, nearly all deforestation itself is
related to meat production.[86] Eighty percent of cleared Amazon forest is
designated as a cattle grazing area to prepare the animals for slaughter, and
the remainder is planted as soy crops used also largely for animal feed.

Every year, we cut down forests as big as England just to raise animals.
That's why our planet's heating up and then many places are having problems
with floods and drought.

A rainforest area the size of a football field is destroyed every second to
produce just 250 hamburgers.[87]

We are losing 55 square meters of rainforest for every beef hamburger
patty.[88]

Forests play a tremendous role in absorbing CO_2. For example, the forests in the Pacific Northwest region of the US are able to absorb half of all the emissions of the state of Oregon, USA.

According to the environmental organization Greenpeace, eight percent of the Earth's forest-related carbon is stored in the vast rainforests of the Congo River Basin in Central Africa. Scientists predict that continued deforestation of the Congo will release the same amount of CO_2 as the United Kingdom emitted over the last 60 years![89] So, it is important to preserve the forest while we still can.

Trees attract rain, keep the soil, and stop the erosion. And [they] give oxygen and shade, and give [a] home to the environmental forest friends, animals, which in turn, also keep our planet going in a good, ecological way.

[Deforestation] is not just [about] the permanent changes to the world's temperature, rainfall and weather patterns, which the forests regulate. It's not just about the millions of people who might lose their livelihoods that depend on the forests. There is more to it than that. There is the extinction of plant and animal species that is 100 times faster than what is natural, and it ruins our ecosystems.

Fortunately, we have the solution ready at hand, which is the organic, vegan solution. We have to accept this organic, vegan solution as the one and only to save our planet right now.

The land for grazing and feed growing could become forests that help reduce global warming. In addition, if all tillable land were turned into organic vegetable farmland, not only would people be fully fed, but up to 40% of all the greenhouse gases in the atmosphere could be absorbed. This is in addition to the elimination of over 50% of emissions caused by livestock raising.[90]

Therefore, in sum, we eliminate most of the human-made greenhouse gases by simply adopting the animal-free, vegan, organic lifestyle.

CONSERVE ENERGY

The Energy Cost of Meat Production

Meat production is energy intensive and grossly energy inefficient. To produce one kilogram of beef consumes 169 mega joules (169-million watts) of energy, or enough energy to drive an average European car for 250 kilometers!

One six-ounce beef steak costs 16 times as much fossil fuel energy as one vegan meal containing three kinds of vegetables and rice.

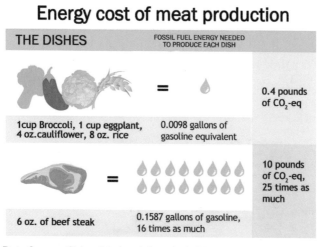

Energy cost of meat production

THE DISHES	FOSSIL FUEL ENERGY NEEDED TO PRODUCE EACH DISH	
1cup Broccoli, 1 cup eggplant, 4 oz. cauliflower, 8 oz. rice	0.0098 gallons of gasoline equivalent	0.4 pounds of CO_2-eq
6 oz. of beef steak	0.1587 gallons of gasoline, 16 times as much	10 pounds of CO_2-eq, 25 times as much

Data Source: Gidon Eshel and Pamela A. Martin, "Diet, Energy, and Global Warming," *Earth Interaction*, Vol 10 (2006), paper No. 9.

The UN IPCC's chair, Dr. Rajendra Pachauri, further points out that meat requires constant refrigerated transportation and storage, the growing and transportation of the animals' food, a lot of packaging, a lot of cooking at high temperatures for long periods, and a whole lot of animal waste products that also need to be processed and disposed of. **Meat production is so costly and inefficient, so unsustainable that it is bad business to produce meat.**[91]

The True Cost of Meat

> "To produce one pound of beef, it takes 2,500 gallons of water, 12 pounds of grain, 35 pounds of topsoil and the energy equivalent of one gallon of gasoline. If all these costs were reflected in the price of the product, without subsidies, the least expensive hamburger in the US would cost US$35." [92]
>
> —John Robbins

RESTORE BIODIVERSITY

> Everything on this planet, including us, is interrelated, and we help each other to make our lives here comfortable and livable. But if we don't know that, we are killing ourselves. Every time we kill a tree or kill an animal, we are killing a little part of ourselves.

Threat Status of Species in Comprehensively Assessed Taxonomic Groups

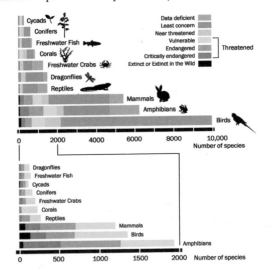

Credit: Secretariat of the Convention on Biological Diversity, *Global Biodiversity Outlook* 3, 2010, http://www.cbd.int/gbo/gbo3/images/GBO3-Figure4-ThreatStatusAssessedGroups.pdf

In the oceans and fresh waterways, so many species of fish have already been lost, with complete aquatic environments such as coral reefs being decimated by such practices as trawling and fishing with explosives. On land, meat consumption is responsible for vast regions being cleared for grazing crops such as soy that are fed to livestock.

With these activities essentially robbing our biodiversity, there has been an alarming rise in the disappearance of plants and animals.[93]

RECLAIM RIVERS AND SOIL FROM POLLUTION

> If we really want to conserve our clean, safe water for ourselves and our children, we must stop livestock production and adopt the plant-based diet.

The US Environmental Protection Agency estimates that agriculture, which is mostly for meat production, contributes to nearly three-quarters of the country's water pollution problems.[94] A single pig farm with say, 500,000 pigs, generates more waste yearly than the 1.5-million residents of Manhattan in New York City. In Virginia State, even the poultry farms are producing 1.5 times more polluting nitrogen than all the people living in the same area. There's no law to regulate these.

The 1.8-million pigs in Ireland generate more waste than the whole country's entire population of 4.2 million!

As the land cannot absorb it all, much of the excess runs into our rivers and soil. We are talking about a horrific amount of toxic material that poses an appalling set of problems, including poisonous gases like hydrogen sulphide and ammonia, residues of pesticides, hormones, antibiotics and bacteria like E. coli that could, and do, cause food poisoning and also death.

Along with the waste are chemical fertilizers runoff used on crops fed to animals, which have been documented by scientists to cause dead zones as well as toxic algae outbreaks, those green moss that grow in the water.

One such event just occurred in Brittany, France, where a majority of the country's livestock and a third of the dairy farms are located. On the Brittany coast, this waste and chemical runoff coming into the sea causes outbreaks of toxic algae, which emit the lethal, deadly gas hydrogen sulfide. So, recently in news we heard of a horse that died within half a minute of stepping into the algae and now the health concerns of over 300 people are being investigated for the same reason around that area.

Making all of this worse is the fact that animal waste is largely unregulated, meaning that there is nothing to stop these events of contamination that can cause illnesses or even death for massive numbers of animals and people.

(Please see to Appendix 9 for more examples of pollution from animal waste.)

ALLEVIATE FINANCIAL AND HEALTH COSTS

Save Trillions in Climate-Change-Mitigation Costs

Leaders are worried about the cost of mitigating climate change. However, the good news is if the world shifted to animal-free diet, then we could reduce the cost by half or more. That means we would reduce tens of trillions of US dollars.

- **The Cost of Climate Change**

> "European Commission study estimates climate change could cost up to US$74 trillion. One-meter sea level rise would increase storm property damage by US$1.5 trillion."[95]
>
> — *Environmental scientists F. Ackerman and E. Stanton*

> "Cost of inaction could reach US$176 billion annually by 2100 for Japan."[96]
>
> —*Prof. Nobuo Mimura and colleagues*

- **Vegan-Diet Savings**

> Global adoption of the vegan diet could wipe 80% (US$32 trillion) off the estimated US$40-trillion cost of mitigating climate change by 2050.[97]

Minimize Health Costs

The health risks of eating meat are more and more evident these days. Livestock are routinely given excessive hormones and antibiotics, which then when consumed as meat can in turn endanger human health.

There are also toxic byproducts in slaughter places such as ammonia and hydrogen sulfide. These poisonous substances have caused deaths among workers due to their extreme toxicity.

As a so-called food, meat is simply one of the most unhealthy, poisonous, unhygienic items that could ever be ingested by humans. We should never eat meat at all if we love and cherish our health and our life. We will live longer without meat, healthier, wiser without meat.

Meat has been scientifically shown to cause all kinds of cancers, also heart disease, high blood pressure, stroke and obesity. The list goes on and on and on. All these diseases kill millions of people every year, millions, millions of people die due to meat-related diseases, and making millions of others seriously sick and disabled as well. There is no end to tragedies caused by the meat diet. We should know this by now through all the scientific and medical evidence.

We did not even mention the filthy conditions, the confined environments where the animals are kept until their slaughter, which promote the transmission of diseases such as the swine flu virus. In fact, some meat-transmitted diseases, like the human form of mad cow disease, are tragically fatal in every case. Whoever contracts mad cow disease is doomed to die sadly and sorrowfully. Other contaminants such as E. coli, salmonella, etc., can also cause serious health problems, long-term damage, sometimes even leading to death.

In a vegan world, there would be no more sad news about someone's child dying of brain damage or paralysis due to E. coli, the deadly bacteria which originally almost always come from farmed animals. There would be no more heartache due to deadly swine flu pandemic, or mad cow disease, cancer, diabetes, strokes and heart attacks, salmonella, Ebola, etc., etc. Even AIDS that we fear so much is originally also from hunting animals to eat. Animal diseases from the horrid, filthy livestock-raising environment are responsible for 75% of all the emerging, infectious human diseases.

Even milk, which we have been told officially to be good for us, is on the contrary poison and causing diseases (and of course financial loss). Here are some: bacterial microbes, pesticides, and enzymes found in cheese, derived from the inner stomach linings of other animals; breast, prostate and testicular cancer from hormones present in milk; listeria and Crohn's disease; hormones and saturated fat leading to osteoporosis, obesity, diabetes and heart disease.

- **Health Cost of Meat and Dairy**

> Cardiovascular Disease has cost $503.2 billion in the US in 2010.[98]
>
> Cancer treatment costs $6.5 billion in the US per year.
>
> Diabetes treatment costs $174 billion in the US per year.
>
> Individual treatment of being overweight costs $93 billion in the US per year.[99]

BUY TIME FOR GREEN TECHNOLOGIES

We cannot cut CO_2 that quick because we don't have other technological inventions right now to replace the ones that we have. How many electric cars do you see running on the United States streets yet? How much CO_2 does that cut? Not much. But the methane pollution came from livestock raising, so if we stop that, no more heating!

There is already some advanced science to capture CO_2 and mix it with sea water to create cement. That will reduce CO_2 used by other cement-producing methods as well and also reduce new CO_2 from polluting the air. But still, any new technology takes so long to develop and to be in the market.

The natural landscapes of grassland and forest are more effective to absorb CO_2 than carbon-capturing technology, according to the UN Environmental Program. Besides, it's risky, I think. It's not tested yet. What if the carbon leaks back into the atmosphere again in a concentrated amount like that? When we capture them year after year, decade after decade, and then something happens, and it leaks up, then what do we do?

So, with the vegan diet, we eat what's best for our health, for the animals, for the environment, and nature will do the rest to restore the balance and save our world.[100]

II. IT IS THE FASTEST AND GREENEST SOLUTION

COOL THE PLANET IMMEDIATELY

Marianne Thieme, co-founder of the Party for Animals in the Netherlands, has outlined clearly the environmental gains of reducing meat in the diet. For example, if all Britons refrain from meat for seven days a week, that would be equivalent to turning half of the country's 25-million households into zero-emission homes. For six days a week, it would be the same as the country's 29-million cars being removed totally from the roads.

- **Comparison with the Conventional Omnivore Diet**

    - An organic [meat-based] diet produces 8% savings in GHG emissions
    - An animal-free, vegan diet produces less than 1/7 the GHG emissions of a meat diet—86% savings in GHG emissions.
    - An organic vegan diet produces 94% savings in GHG emissions.[101]

    —The Foodwatch report on the greenhouse effect of conventional and organic farming in Germany

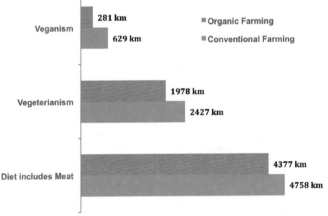

The Organic Vegan Diet's Emissions Savings

Greenhouse effect from different kinds of eating habits, per capita and per annum, presented in car kilometeres*

Veganism	281 km / 629 km
Vegeterianism	1978 km / 2427 km
Diet includes Meat	4377 km / 4758 km

■ Organic Farming
■ Conventional Farming

*equivalent to the CO$_2$ emissions of a BMW 118d with 119g CO$_2$/km

Data source: Foodwatch Organic: A Climate Saviour? The Foodwatch report on the greenhouse effect of conventional and organic farming in Germany. May 2009, p. X.

[Therefore,] the greenest of all the green policy, the greenest of all the green action, the most compassionate, the most heroic, the lifesaving action, is the vegan diet.

The reason is based on the significant, planet-cooling effect of removing methane from the atmosphere, which happens when we switch to the organic vegan diet. And besides removing the harmful methane emissions, organic tilling methods can actually store 40% of the carbon back into the soil. So to be veg is a way to not only eliminate significant emissions, but to absorb even more carbon from the atmosphere.

And with that approach, we are working toward being able to save the world. Because the switch to the animal-free diet removes all the methane production and its associated pollutants, to say nothing of the animal cruelty, it will help reverse these planetary disasters, such as the tsunamis, the floods, storms, typhoons and the landslides, etc., etc.

In fact, the head of the United Nations Framework Convention on Climate Change, Mr. Yvo de Boer, already stated in June 2008 that "The best solution would be for us all to become vegetarians." He meant vegans.

BE VEGAN: THE GREENEST LIFESTYLE

[Stopping meat production] saves 80% of the total cost of US$40 trillion for reducing global warming; uses 4.5 times less land to grow food; conserves up to 70% clean water; saves 80% of the cleared Amazonian rainforest from animal grazing. A solution for world hunger: Free up to 3.4-billion hectares of land; free up to 760-million tons of grain every year (that is half the world's grain supply.) Conserves one-third fossil fuel used for meat production; reduces pollution from untreated animal waste; maintains cleaner air; saves 4.5 tons of emissions per US household per year; stops 80% of global warming or more. The list goes on.

A study conducted in the United States found that organic farming preserves topsoil and keeps water bodies clean, and if used worldwide, would have the potential to absorb and store approximately 40% of all present-day, CO_2 emissions each year. This would be a direct benefit to our Earth.

Other aspects of vegan, organic farming that are beneficial include things like crop rotation, mulching and natural fertilizers. Crop rotation means that a field is planted each season with different crops. This variety approach helps keep the plants healthy and also restores fertility and nutrients to the soil. Other methods such as mulching and even a new method called no-till organic farming help retain moisture and reduce soil erosion considerably.

So, in general, vegan, organic farming follows a philosophy of living in harmony with nature and protection for the planet and all beings. The methods employed support the natural balance between farming and the environment. Over time, the combination of this care and practice through the techniques available can go a long way toward restoring the balance from problems that may have arisen in the past.

EATING LOCAL PRODUCE AND EATING ORGANIC MEAT?

Interestingly, studies show that eating locally is not as good as eating vegan. For example, scientists at Carnegie Mellon University calculated that a vegan diet reduced over seven times the emissions compared to a 100% local meat diet. So, eating vegan is better than eating local even.

In another study, Foodwatch in Germany found that switching from a meat diet to an organic meat diet saved only 8% of emissions, but switching to a non-organic, vegan diet, even non-organic, vegan diet, reduced 86% of emissions.[102] So, we save the planet by being vegan. Even non-organic! So, actually, organic is good, local is wonderful, but the first step is at least being vegan, organic or not.

Even organic meat is actually not eco-friendly at all; it requires even more land, and more energy than the non-organic meat in meat farming. Can you believe that? So, it doesn't even help to try to raise animals organically. The so-called "sustainable," "free-range," organic poultry, for example, needs 20% more energy and has a 20% higher, bigger impact on global warming than non-organic poultry farms. Think about that. So, we've been misled all the time.

III. GIVE LIFE TO SAVE LIFE

Before we expect the lion to lay down peacefully with
the lamb, we humans must do it first.

MEAT EATING KILLS BOTH ANIMALS AND HUMANS

Eating meat is the biggest cruelty one can ever commit even to ourselves.
Even if we don't kill the animals ourselves, we are still responsible for their
deaths.

For meat we kill literally billions [of animals.] A staggering 55-billion
animals, eight times the entire global human population are killed for
human consumption each and every year.[103] This is not even counting the
several billion fish that perish, with a total loss that translates to more than
155-million beings killed every day.

Dairy is included together with meat because the cruelty and torture is
the same, and the end result is a horrible death for the poor animals. There
is no mercy in the dairy industry either.

Humans die, too, each year because of meat and fish, and anything
related to animal consumption. Nearly 33-million people succumb to meat-
related diseases annually through heart disease, cancer and other conditions
that claim the lives of more than 90,000 persons each day.

And then there are those who cannot obtain food because the grains
they need are used to feed animals that will be killed for meat. There are
25,000 people who die of hunger indirectly, also because of meat.[104]

We have hundreds of thousands of people die each year as the victims of
meat-caused global warming. And we have tens of millions of others who
are made homeless due to climate change. We call them climate refugees, if
there is such a term; in fact, they have no status.

And this is not including the innocent wildlife and domestic animals
who suffer because of meat-related problems.

**Meat causes global warming and kills, and kills and kills. Therefore,
MEAT is murder, a crime that must be stopped.**

ANIMAL SLAUGHTER: A CRIME OF GLOBAL PROPORTIONS

There is no bigger moral crisis than the one that is created by the mass massacring of sweet, innocent living beings for our pleasure when we have other choices. Such mass murder is a crime of global proportions. And this killing energy in turn breeds and strengthens other negative energy, which is degrading our society and destroying our world.

We have produced a lot, a lot, and a lot of negative energy by killing billions and billions of innocent sentient lives, and killing millions of our fellow humans even, over millennia, directly or indirectly. Directly is through war. Indirectly is through disease that we made ourselves, like with the bubonic plague, pneumonic plague, and now swine flu, bird flu, etc.

It is not a coincidence that the main cause of global warming is meat eating. And many of the leading health problems in our world are also derived from meat eating. So meat eating is cruelty to animals. Meat eating is cruelty to our well-being. Meat eating is cruelty to our children's well-being. Meat eating is cruelty to the planet. Be vegan, and we will never have to suffer many of these kinds of consequences ever, ever again.

We have to stop the killing of men or animals. We have to stop producing animal products. And we have to stop using it. **Three stops: stop killing, stop producing, stop using.** And stop eating it, of course, stop eating the meat.

When people understand the gruesome truth behind animal farming and the innocence of all the animals who sacrifice their lives, it is easy to see that eating the dead flesh of another being is not only unnecessary, it leaves us with a trail of bloody footprints.

RESTORE HARMONY WITH NATURE

We should all remember that we share this planetary abode, the water, the air, the resources, the food; all of nature, we share only. Be veg, go green and save their planet too, the planet of the animals. This is truly the best way to restore our environment and ensure the highest degree of peace.

> "We are part of the Earth and she is a part of us.
> The fragrant flowers are our sisters; the deer,
> the horse, the great eagle, are our brothers.
> What is man without the animals?"
>
> "If all animals disappear, humankind would die of a
> great spiritual loneliness. The rocky peaks, the humid
> countryside furrows, the physical warmth between horse
> and man—they all belong to the same family.
> Earth does not belong to man; it is man
> who belongs to the Earth."
>
> —*Chief Sealth, Duwamish Native American Chief, after whom the*
> *city of Seattle in Washington State, U.S.A. is named*

Imagine our planet without animals at all. All the dogs gone, cats gone, birds gone, fish gone, buffalos gone, elephants gone; imagine, none of the animals survive, how would we live? How would our life feel abundant? It would feel very dry and meaningless.

So, if we respect all life, then we also don't take any life. The Earth provides in plenty for humans and for animals. We don't need to take in a way that hurts or harms any other being. That means the animal-free diet, again and again and again.

If all humanity lives with the animal-free diet, and lives in respect for nature and other life, then we will have a Heaven on Earth. Everything will be forgiven. Everything will be well and good. The planet will be restored, the animals will be thankful, the humans will be healthy, and all will be happy and blessed. That's all there is to do, be veg.

ANIMALS BRING LOVE TO THE WORLD

The animals really come to help mankind. Like the Bible said, "I make them to befriend you and be your helpers." It's truly like that. But not every human can avail of this help and that's a pity. Instead, they kill them.

Anything God puts on Earth is for a purpose. We should not kill anything. We should not eat anything except a plant-based diet.

The animals come to this planet with a special role. Many of them are able to bring down divine power from Heaven, or love, just through their presence. Some, like horses and rabbits, can protect their human caregivers from negative influences, or boost them with good health, good luck, even material fortune, joy or spiritual upliftment. They watch out for us quietly, and humbly send blessings our way. Some of them are from higher levels of consciousness; they only came down in animal form to help humankind or other beings on Earth.

Animals also have very noble, vital roles in the physical realm. Some animals, like zebras, monkeys, and wild parrots help to disperse the seeds, while bees and other insects help to pollinate crops and other plants, and others maintain the health of the forests and oceans. Animals directly help humans as well.

I read in the newspapers, I heard on the radio, I saw on TV, so many noble animals that rescue people. They rescue their own kin at the expense of their own life. So we should learn from all these golden animals.

(Please see Appendix 10 for Supreme Master Ching Hai's spiritual insights on the NQ or Noble Quality and LQ or Loving Quality of animals and humans.)

CREATE EDEN ON EARTH

With the organic, vegan lifestyle as part of everyone's heroic mission, our efforts together will surely bring a safe and saved world for both humans and our beloved animal co-inhabitants.

It will be like Eden on Earth where everyone has equal access to community services as well as community resources. And everything will be distributed evenly. And everyone will be respected and loved and taken care of exactly like the next one or the last one or the first one.

Dialogue between Master and Disciple:

Q: Master, Would you kindly explain as to how a loving relationship between humans and animals would affect our planet?

M: Well, that will be a big peace on Earth, I mean capital PEACE.

4

ENACTING VEGAN LAWS AND POLICIES

> I hope the governments would please make it into law to forbid the killing of animals, to forbid anymore animal livestock raising.
>
> If they are truly the leaders that pledge to protect their people, to improve their country in many aspects, then this is the first step we have to do.
>
> Stop the meat industry, stop the fish industry, stop the dairy industry. Then our planet will be the way it was and even better.

I. WORLD LEADERS SHOULD SET AN EXAMPLE

BE VEGAN

I would say to them [the world leaders] to use their mighty power to change the diet of the planet. And adopt immediately, new technology, sustainable energy. And set an example by themselves by becoming a vegetarian or vegan. Change their diet. Use their mighty power. Use their example, to set a new diet for the planet, the vegetarian (vegan) diet.[105]

They first have to be vegetarian (vegan), and then they use their power truly. Like the way they forbid smoking. They could do that by forbidding meat as well, by citing all the harm that meat would do to humans and the planet. They can do that, just like forbidding smoking.

ACT IN ACCORDANCE WITH THE PRINCIPLE OF LOVE

The leaders must change themselves also, and then in turn change our social system so that it becomes more free and more spiritual, more morally high. Because they carry with them this responsibility—it's heavy if they do not act with Heaven's merciful nature and progressive plan, and if they then do not act according to the principle of the universe.

The first principle, the most important, that is the principle of love. Anything they do according to this principle, then it's good. I mean good for other people. Progress for people and protection for all and respect for all life—that is according to the principle of love. Anything else against that is bound to bring disaster for themselves and for their countries, or the planet as a whole.

If these leaders try and go into more spiritual aspect to find their real Self, they will know that they're so glorious, so benevolent, so loving, so kind, so wise and so Godlike. Then they will see the rewards themselves. But it depends on how great their help to humankind or animals and the environment is, and how much is their sincerity. If they try their best to help the world, and the number of people that are helped by them, and their sincerity, is great, it is of course the glorious Heaven that will be awaiting them, accordingly. God knows our heart and deeds, you see?

II. GOVERNMENTS MUST TAKE URGENT ACTION

The leaders of the nations must do something. The people of all nations must do something. Just because we can still sit here pretty and talk, just because in our area there is not yet water shortage or food prices going up doesn't mean it will not happen to us soon.

We have to do something to avoid the tragedy that is already happening to billions of other people. There are one-billion people hungry already because of climate change, and short of water and food. Please take action now; very simple. Just be veg. Just be veg is truly enough for now, and it will be enough for a long future to come.

DISTRIBUTE INFORMATION ABOUT THE PLANT-BASED LIFESTYLE

People are not really well-informed about what's on their plate. Mostly the little, packed meat that went on their plate doesn't resemble anything of where it came from.

The so-called tradition keeps passing on from one generation to the next. And the whole society just supports it as a natural way of life. So now people have become more aware of the cruelty that we measure upon animals. So I think we, people, turn to more compassion and respect for all life.

Many don't realize the harmful emissions of the livestock industry or that killing begets killing, and they are not aware that meat is another kind of addictive poison. They are not aware that meat is destroying our planet.

The governments have to explain to people that it's truly harmful now and this is an emergency that people should stop eating meat. **It's not a matter of personal choice anymore. It's a planetary life—and-death matter.**

In the case of imminent disaster, the governments would evacuate people in no time. And in the case of war, people are always informed how to protect themselves. The governments even recruit new army members so that they can go out and protect the country or go out to war.

So, in this case, it's even more urgent than war. I'm sure the government will have a solution to it. I'm sure the people can be informed anywhere in the nation. The government has the power that's vested in them to do this.

The governments have to help. Distribute more information encouraging more vegetarian diet lifestyle, just bombarding the whole planet with a new energy of compassion and love and health and then everybody will join in. Supportive energy is very important.

They have to publicize it everywhere. They have to give leaflets to people to read, make it a public job to do it. They have to give an official endorsement and let everybody know about the benefit of the vegetarian diet. They have to create websites for vegetarian menus, all free of charge, class for vegetarian cooking, vegetarian clubs. **Make it official, and then everybody would follow like a happy trend, some new change in the world.**

The most important thing is that humankind and all citizens around the world should know the great benefit of becoming vegetarian to save the Earth. They should know how dangerous and how urgent our current situation is. This is the most important thing.

They should also know how much benefit the vegetarian diet, the non-killing diet, can bring to humankind, let alone the moral aspect. Firstly, we talk about how the vegetarian diet benefits our health and saves the planet, then our children would have a home to live in the future.

We only have this one home: Earth. If it is destroyed, another one cannot be built, unlike a house, which can be rebuilt, we can't build another Earth if it's destroyed. It's not that easy. Therefore, the most important thing for the government to do is to spread information to the public.

BAN MEAT AS SMOKING WAS BANNED

> Vegetarianism should be a way of life. There shouldn't be discussion any more.

We have to ban meat. We're banning it now by showing people how to eat, to cook vegetarian. We go all out. This is really for survival. Make it your mission in life to inform people about the danger of eating meat and show them the solution.

They banned cigarettes and it's banned. And they banned drugs and it's banned. The same with the climate change policy. If they just do what they know is good, then it's very quick. In no time we will recover or we'll stop the effect.

Because if we don't raise anymore cattle or animals then the Earth will be more sustainable: no more greenhouse gas or methane gas from the animals, no more multiplying all the time. Whatever [animals] we have already, we keep it, and no more raising for profit and meat. Then the Earth will recover. After a while, the cows will be gone the natural way, and then all the land will be planted with trees, vegetables again.

If we compare the trend to tobacco, which is another killer substance like meat, only after 1950, when the first major research came out showing that tobacco causes lung cancer, the government started to implement smoking bans, gradually more and more until today; more than 80 countries have some kind of public smoking ban.[106]

Studies show that the smoking bans actually helped people to quit smoking, and the quitters were happier because of the ban, because they know that their habit was bad for them.

Similarly, a ban on meat, which we all now know from the studies, is a very bad habit which kills us and our children, our loved ones, and is killing our planet.

So, a ban of meat will be a strong current to carry the trend toward a vegan world.

Because a good leader stops what is bad for the people and facilitates what is good for them. They can facilitate, namely, through public campaigns, using the media, and through schools to inform about the benefits of the healthy, life-saving, planet-saving way of life.

WE HAVE NO OTHER CHOICE

Either We Change or We Will All Go

First of all, we have to know that we have no choice but to change, either that or the planet. Either we change, or we will all go. There's no choice anymore.

If we don't stop the livestock-raising and meat-eating practice, we will not be able to save the planet, including them and their meat business. So, I think we have to choose between our lives and a career. We have to survive first. We have to think of the planet people as a whole, not just some business. It is truly that urgent.

Given this critical necessity, these people who are economically tied to the meat industry would be willing to change if they were properly informed and know how important it is to change their lifestyle and their career. They have many strong motivations. For example, the first is to save the planet from a climate catastrophe, save all lives in this world.

If we don't stop it, we will continue on a course toward total disaster and mass extinction, affecting everyone, whether you are in the business of meat, transportation for it, etc. or not or a related job of the meat industry.

Stop Animal Killing and Wars and Rebuild the Country

The thing is, the leaders should know what is a priority. What's the use of worrying about war or about position or about anything else when the planet is going to be ruined? So right now, all the leaders must concentrate on saving our planet and must concentrate on spreading information and making new laws for people to live a more benevolent life.

There's no need even laws, but the law is maybe better, just more concrete; otherwise, people are ready. Just the governments have to implement some more rules and reminding people to be good, to be virtuous, to adhere to the law of love like not killing animals, not eating animals, and not doing anything harmful to animals or other humans or even the environment.

It has to be more concrete and more dynamic action. First, all wars must stop. Money and goods must be only to sustain and nourish all beings—have to distribute all the goods of the planet to all. For example, even if no war, the related money could feed the whole world, free of charge, for many decades.

And all killing, torturing humans or animals must stop. All deforestation, harming the environment and destroying the trees, all that has to stop. And leaders will only bring into law what's beneficial, peaceful, if possible, spiritual as well, for all, if possible, like protecting true spiritual groups, the harmless but beneficial groups.

Share wealth among all: Distribute enough food and clothing for needy humans and animals. Building protective areas for all, for humans and animals—protect all lives. Rebuild forests, clean up rivers, lakes, oceans and protect them; award to green and animal care groups. Clear away, clean up alcohol and drugs, meat and animal products. Laboratory tests involving cruelty to animals must stop. Clear away animal-factory farms. Make inmates or soldiers as well to go help people, plant vegetables or do productive works. Promote and help organic vegetable farming. Give subsidies for education, health-related areas.

And weapon production business must decrease to zero. Clean up our society of all shady and detrimental products and activities. Provide security and comfort to all, so no one would commit offenses for lack of basic necessities and education. Erase borders and provide all the same status and respect of citizenship.

If [the governments] even have to keep any armies, then they have to retrain them for helping people in disaster in urgent cases and to rebuild homes wherever necessary, and helping people in their time of need. All these have to be done and more even. Anything that helps other people, helps the citizens, and helps the animals and environment, all the governments, the leaders have to try their best to implement the actions for that, and they have to do it now already.

THE MEAT INDUSTRY IS A LOSING BUSINESS

It is Inefficient in the Use of Energy and Resources

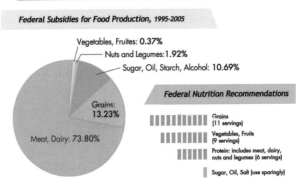

Data Source: Physicians Committee for Responsible Medicine, "Health vs. Pork: Congress Debates the Farm Bill, "*Good Medicine*, Vol. XVI, 4 (Autumn 2007). www.pcrm.org/magazine/gm07autumn/health_pork.html

The industry is bad, bad, bad business, [and] is not lucrative at all for the whole planet, for everybody. It's a most inefficient business, with very high production costs for electricity, water and grains to produce the same amount of so-called "food," which is replaceable. We have better food than meat.

It Depends on Subsidies and Tax Revenue

For example, if the government didn't give them any subsidies for the meat industry in any case, then a hamburger that some people eat produced by clearing forests in India alone would cost US$ 200![107]

In the US, even before the swine flu impacted the pig-farming business, the pig industry had been losing billions of dollars. Why? Because they cannot afford the grains to feed their livestock due to the high food prices, and the food prices are getting higher and higher nowadays. So, how do they survive? Your tax money goes to the government, and the government subsidizes them. So, it's a losing business.

Everywhere, from the US to China, the government has to subsidize animal farmers by paying them at least tens of billions of US dollars every year![108] But that's your money that you're eating! If you can eat that and be healthy, happy, then it would be reasonable. But it's not!

It Comes with Heavy Medical Costs

These hamburgers contain all parts of the animals that you don't know where they even come from, and contain all kinds of bacteria, all kinds of diseases.[109] If you want information from the medical journals or medical scientists, they will tell you all this. Not only do we pay a lot of tax money into the subsidies for the meat industry, we pay a lot more tax money for the hospitalization, for the burying of our loved ones, for the heartache that we have to bear the whole lifetime for losing one of our dearest, or many of our dearest.

It Inflicts Immense Suffering on Animals

All this suffering is unnecessary for our fragile body to bear. If we avoid meat, we will avoid all that—the money for hospital, medicine. And not only that, before we get the medicine we make more animals suffer by experimenting with them by vivisection, by injecting chemicals into their bodies, by making them suffer, torturing to no end just to obtain the medicine that we feel safe for human use. And again, it's still not safe for human use.

All this suffering, all this tax money goes into different directions. It doesn't help you at all. It's just wasting resources, finance and national strength, and human's health and happiness. It's just a waste. It's just a very, very, very bad business.

The meat industry is terribly harmful to us in every imaginable situation, in any imaginable aspect. Now, if the subsidies are not going in to support them, the farmers of the animal-raising industry could not make ends meet with their business. They would have gone out of business already. So, I suggest the government doesn't give any more subsidies to animal-raising industry. Instead, tell them to convert into vegan farmers.

Meat-Industry Jobs Endanger Workers

Besides all that, for the majority of the workers in the meat business, it's not a safe working place either. It's one of the most dangerous jobs with some of the highest rates of injury and exposure to chemicals and diseases like influenza, swine flu, bird flu and mad cow disease, which is always fatal, always deadly.

Now, we have to ask ourselves: Is it all worth it? This is not to talk about the effect on the meat consumers in terms of all the sickness—cancers, diabetes and health problems, and heart diseases. Almost all diseases that you can name come from the meat diet or related. So, given a better choice for livelihood, wouldn't we choose the one that helps ourselves and others stay healthy, over a profession that made people and ourselves sick and die young?

> "The powerful myth that industrial food is cheap and affordable only survives because all of these environmental, health, and social costs are not added to the price of industrial food. When we calculate the real price, it is clear that far from being cheap, our current food production system is imposing staggering monetary burdens on us and future generations."[110]
>
> — AlterNet.Org

Banning Meat is the Only Way to Save the Planet

Everything to do with compassionate living is good for you and it's pleasing to Heaven. And it will save the planet. It's not just good business, it will save the planet, and it will save countless lives, now and in the future, including the ones involved in the meat business. That's why the Buddha named the meat business as one of the five businesses that people should not engage in.

The meat business is a bad business. It's very bad for you. And the other four are: business in weapons, business in human trafficking, business in intoxicants and business in poison. All these harmful businesses are bad for you, now and in the future.

ENCOURAGE, SUPPORT AND SUBSIDIZE ORGANIC FARMING

[The government] could encourage the farmers to grow crops and give them subsidies to grow vegetables replacing the loss of meat. The more they grow, the more subsidies they get. And the farmers also have to be explained that they would be doing the world a great service.

They would be a great hero, the world savers, if they grow vegetables to feed humans instead of raising animals, and let the animals be. The government has to tell them that they have to treat the animals with all kindness until they have gone back to Heaven naturally.

At present, this practice is not widely spread and encouraged by the government or by the media. So, in my humble opinion, instead of subsidies for the farmers who lose money on meat or because the meat was tainted with disease or something, the government can subsidize the farmers so they have more financial support to fall on until this becomes more stabilized as a practice and the market has more demand for organic food. Then farmers will be happy to grow more vegetarian food to supply for the health of humans and the planet.

The government can give them vegetable seeds and training on better ways to farm without using chemical fertilizers, because sometimes the farmers are just not well informed about the harms of livestock raising, or the chemicals or the fertilizers or insecticides.

[The farmers] are not informed about a better way to grow vegetables and make more profit. The government can help them implement the measures to conserve the land and improve the quality of their products so that their buyers will trust in them, etc. The government can also set up a certification and quality standardization system to further promote the organic, vegan industry.

Organic Farming is Easy to Implement

Right now, organic food is very in. And it's very healthy for everybody. And it's in very big demand.

In our Association, we have many members who are doing organic farming. And it's proven that anyone can do it. Anyone who is interested can log on to our website to know all the information how to do organic farming. It's so easy, so simple; don't even need much water at all. And the food grows so fast, and even one or two persons can take care of many hectares without much problem at all.

We tell people to do organic farming, how to conserve rainwater, ground water, and conserve land, planting trees to attract rain, etc. In the Alwar district of Rajasthan, India, one Indian village was able to guide the water enough that it brought back to life five flowing rivers—five flowing rivers—that had been dead before, been dried up before due to withdrawing too much water. We could learn from them as well.

We have the www.SupremeMasterTV.com to inform everyone who is interested in it. It's not much capital needed even. Even if capital is needed, the government should give them subsidies to help the organic farmer instead of using that to help the meat production, which is harmful to us. To help organic farming is helpful to everybody including the farmer.

Supply Vegan School Meals and Support Local Food Co-ops

From what I understand, complete systems where the schools are connected to the farmers in a sustainable way are perhaps being developed, but not fully exercised.

There is a program that began in Europe and Japan and it's now also in the US, where a group of individuals such as those belonging to a food cooperative develop a relationship with a farmer or the farmers, who agree to supply them with fresh produce. The farmers then grow a variety of food and people purchase from a variety of whatever is fresh.

This has become very popular and, in many places it has a waiting list even. So the farms are usually sustainably-run, organic farms. It is a good situation because the people are getting healthy food that they can trust while supporting the farmers' livelihood and often the environment at the same time.

I am sure if the governments support organic farming, it will be a trend in no time.

If the governments lead the way with the message that this is how to be green, and how to protect the planet, then the farmers would be happy to grow more vegan food.

To spread the practice of organic farming would help in so many ways.

The Benefits of Organic Vegan Farming

The benefits of organic farming for human livelihood, for human health and for animals' health, natural resources and protection of our planet, all these benefits we cannot even underestimate, we cannot even estimate all in here. Organic farming not only helps to protect the planet, it will even help to eliminate hunger.

Returning to traditional, organic farming methods is already proven by success in Africa, for example, and in some places like the Americas, Europe and Australia. Organic vegan farming is growing very, very fast, and is very, very profitable right now, because there is a growing demand. People are more informed about the harms of the meat and more informed about the benefits of a vegetarian diet. So organic, vegan, vegetable farming should be very, very, very good for anyone who wants to switch business.

Also, there are many successful stories for organic farming already across the continent of Africa. For example, in the area surrounding Cape Town, South Africa, the townships are growing 100% organic gardens, with crops that are sold locally.[111] A similar operation has begun in Kenya. And in Uganda, where organic fertilizers were recently introduced, they are already seeing success with the soil and harvest.[112]

On the Supreme Master Television, we also feature a whole section about organic farming, on our website as well, www.SupremeMasterTV.com. On this website, we share a lot of info about how to do organic farming, which is very profitable, costs less water, a lot less work and is very beneficial to our health, to the workers and to the planet.

If you eat organic vegetables, you will hardly have to go to the hospital and all the money we can save to better education for the children, better care for the elderly, and building more beautiful roads, more equipment, inventions, and use it more for sustainable energies, for free for everybody. Free energy for everybody, free education for all the children, free care for all the elderly and free food for all the one-billion, at least, hungry people in the world. The benefit has no end.

Sustainability and High Yields

It has been found that a large-scale change to organic farming could feed the world. Research in Denmark and elsewhere has shown larger yields from organic farming on land that was previously underutilized.[113]

In fact, the large yields produced by conventional farming are taken at the expense of the soil, of our health, and of the environment. And these enormous, single crops, such as soy, are mostly produced to feed animals for meat production, not for humans' consumption.

In Africa, the United Nations Environment Program did a study in which they found crop yields were doubled when the small farmers used organic farming methods.[114] In this case, since the organic practices such as composting and rotating crops improve the soil instead of buying fertilizers and pesticides, the organic farmers can use their money to buy better seeds.

Another research in the US found that organic farming methods could be used to triple farm yields. One of the main factors in enabling the high yields was the farmers were planting legumes, like beans or soya beans, cover crops between growing seasons, which fixed enough natural nitrogen in the soil to ensure high crop yields. [115]

With the world food shortage continuing to worsen, more people are going hungry every day, so if we just stop the animal-raising practices, and if we don't feed all the corn and all the cereals and vegetables to the animals, all the food that we produce right now could feed two-billion people already.

Reducing the Use of Pesticides and Fertilizers

[Organic farming] is even good for animals, all beings on this planet, including even trees and land, in part because it does not use chemical fertilizer or pesticides, many of which are considered by the United States Environment Protection Agency and the European Union to be potentially cancer-causing and also depleting of our bees' colonies and killing many others animals that we cannot even all name here.

One of the US studies indicate that if the United States' eight-million acres of produce farms went organic, then the risk of consuming dietary pesticides would be reduced by 97%. Can you imagine? Chemical fertilizer and pesticide runoff are also known to contribute to the ocean dead zones. We are killing our planet by pesticides and chemical fertilizer. [116]

Over five-billion pounds of pesticides are used throughout the world each year! And only about 10%—10%—of these chemicals even reach the areas where they are intended for. So the rest goes into the air and water where they have been linked to everything from cancer of humans and animals to oceanic dead zones.

In Europe, one pesticide was found to be the reason for billions of bees dying across the continent, while others are known to make the eggshells of birds become thinner, resulting in the death of their babies because the shells crack and break before the baby is ready to be born. [117]

And furthermore, organic produce is free of genetically modified organisms, and its nutrient content is actually higher than that of conventionally grown fruit and vegetables.

Improving the Environment and Soil

If all people, all the farmers and all the arable land on our planet turn into vegan farming methods, then immediately, 40% of the CO_2 will be absorbed by the farming methods alone already.[118]

To switch to organic farming will restore the health of the soil which has been depleted by conventional growing practices. The topsoil stays and proves better at withstanding floods and hurricanes. Wildlife and ecosystems also win. According to the largest study done on organic farming in the UK, compared to conventional farms, organic farms contained 85% more plant species, with 71% taller and thicker hedges, and a healthy return of native animals across the species.[119]

Furthermore, organic, vegan farming will halt the runoff of chemical fertilizers that have created monstrous dead zones in the ocean.

Saving Energy and Resources

Organic, vegan farming is productive, saving 37% more energy and even more water than conventional farming methods.[120]

Saving Money for Governments

The cost of subsidizing organic vegetable farming is very small compared to the subsidies needed to keep the animal farms afloat, meaning just to keep them from losing money and going bankrupt.

Organic, vegan farming can save governments a lot, a lot of money, 80% of it.[121]

Imagine all the tax money coming back to us or going toward building something better; for example, the cost of trying to mitigate a significant portion of the greenhouse gases.

Profitability for Farmers

A study on small farmers in Latin America who switched to organic vegetable farming found that they earned higher revenues than before.[122] According to respected Dutch scientists, tens of trillions of US dollars can be saved by world governments if all the world becomes vegan.[123]

We have also multiple studies in the United States, India and New Zealand. They all have confirmed this, that some of the reasons for the greater profits are that the production costs are lower than conventional farming.

There are more crop varieties that could be rotated, such as corn, soybeans and alfalfa. Also, the organic system is naturally more resistant to drought than conventional farm systems.

Improving Food Safety and Health

Finally, we all benefit from better health because [organic food is] free of toxins and abundant in nutrients, without the genetic modification and cancer-causing pesticides. In contrast to animal products, which are known to cause cancer, heart disease, diabetes, and obesity, etc., organically farmed fruits and vegetables contain abundant nutrients that help us to avoid all these modern conditions. Surely organic, vegan food is the only food we should feel safe, and would feel safe and will feel safe. In fact, we will feel the safest food to give to our children, the best food to give to our children.

[Organic food's] nutrient content is actually higher than that of conventionally grown fruit and vegetables. It is for these reasons that we in our group use as much organic produce as much as possible.

Home-grown organic fruit harvested by a child gardener.

HELP MEAT-INDUSTRY WORKERS MAKE THE TRANSITION TO NEW JOBS

Tell [workers in the meat industry] to do some other job, give them some other new jobs to do and explain to them the benefits of a new life, which is full of health, full of vigor, and peace, love and happiness. Everyone would look forward to that. At least they would try. And then once they try, they know it works. And if everybody else is trying it, their neighbors are trying it, their friends are trying it, then there is a supporting energy, and the whole world will change.

Not breeding [animals] anymore, not to talk about killing them, we have to stop all that. To save the planet, they can do it by stop raising livestock, stop breeding animals and stop butchering them for a living. They will understand if the government really uses their power to explain to them and giving them some other alternatives to live on. Give them the explanation, the subsidies they need, the alternative jobs, or the alternative choice. We have choices.

I suggest that all the [meat industry farmers] keep their pigs or cows as pets. I think we should sterilize them [the animals] so that we don't continue to breed too many animals, because then we would be in the same position right now, or even worse if they keep multiplying.

Nowadays, there are more and more good opportunities for the farmers, retailers, transporters. They just do the same; instead of transporting pigs, they transport organic vegetables, etc. Or the farmer retailers, they could switch from the meat business to organic vegetable farming.

III. ANIMAL FARMERS' SUCCESSFUL TRANSITION TO ALTERNATIVE CAREERS

In the United States

There was one American pig farmer who had owned many pigs all crammed in a filthy factory farm. After being visited by the famous vegan author John Robbins, the famous ice cream heir, and he left his father's business of ice cream, multi-million-dollar business, in order to go into a vegan direction. So, he visited this pig farm, and then this farmer suddenly remembered that in his childhood he truly loved one pig as his close friend and companion, but he was forced to deny and forget this loving feeling due to the pressure of his family and society.[124]

But after realizing it, he could no longer abuse the gentle pigs one more second. He decided to quit. So, instead of raising pigs, he bought a small organic farm and sells organic vegetables, and he's doing fine. He's still alive. And his heart is still more alive than ever.

There was another [who] brings his 10 pet pigs—he has 10 as his pets that he kept from his old farm—and visits schools now often to show the children how intelligent and friendly pigs really are, so the children will not eat the pigs, for example. Not only he doesn't raise pigs anymore, he goes into the opposite direction to protect the animals.

There was a rancher who owned a big ranch of cows, but then suddenly he changed because he had cancer from meat. After he treated himself [from a tumor,] he became vegan, and now he's an animal advocate. He goes everywhere lecturing, telling people the truth, the real truth, the cruel truth and the bad business truth about raising animals. He's a very staunch advocate for animals. His name is Howard Lyman. He was once or twice a guest speaker on the Supreme Master Television.

In the Middle East

Recently in Iran, there was a dairy cow farmer—he even wrote to us telling his story—who also decided that he needed to change his career to help the planet and his own conscience. So, he made sure all his cows were adopted to good, safe homes to live the rest of their dignified lives. And now he works at a vegan restaurant.

In Asia

Another story comes from Formosa (Taiwan), where a pig farmer just became vegan after watching the Supreme Master Television and realizing that he wanted to protect the environment and avoid bad karmic retribution for himself and his family. So right now, he is keeping all his pigs as spoilt family-member pets for life. And he is switching to a different kind of farming.

In all these cases, the people involved are doing just fine, even better than ever before. It took a great amount of courage in the beginning to change their whole life career around, but all of them would guarantee that it was worth it, more than worth it. It's worth the great freedom of their heart, their spirit and happiness of their family as well and health.

IV. Examples of Good Governance

The European Union

The European Parliament admits that the meat diet is the cause for global warming, and they will reconsider to cut the subsidy for the meat industry, and instead they give it to the organic farmers, etc.[125]

Though it's not going as quickly as I would like, but it looks like the critical mass is doing something because there is progress being made. Some courageous, brave, heroic leaders are helping to make the change, which is very touching and inspiring.

And Jens Holm, Member of the European Parliament has been working to get measures adopted in the European Union that recommend reducing meat to lower greenhouse gas emissions.[126]

Germany

Germany's Environment Minister visited Brazil to help enact stricter regulations for preventing deforestation for meat that's being exported to Europe.

Ireland

There are many who convert themselves into organic farmers right now. In Ireland, the Agriculture Minister wrote to all the farmers in Ireland to tell them to convert themselves into organic farming, vegetable farming, and they subsidize them even. Right now there's a huge percentage of farmers converting themselves into organic farming.

Belgium

One of Belgium's largest cities, Ghent, officially declared every Thursday a veggie day, and starting this school year all city schools will have vegetarian meals every Thursday.[127]

The United Kingdom

I am grateful to His Royal Highness Prince Charles for his forthright courage and fearless eloquence in speaking out on the environment. I really respect him, salute him. He is also a man of action and ahead of his time.

For example, he opened an organic produce market and is trying very hard to halt deforestation of the rainforest worldwide.

Prince Charles is also trying to minimize his own carbon footprint, such as in his transportation. He also donated from his own fund US$2.8 billion—that's almost three- billion dollars—for forest preservation.[128]

I commend humbly the UK government for all its leadership and laud all its projects toward the country's low emissions future.

I would like to highlight the government's important work in sustainable food policy. As early as July 2008, a report commissioned by Prime Minister Gordon Brown to evaluate the UK's food policy acknowledged that "a healthy, low-impact diet would contain less meat and fewer dairy products than we typically eat today."[129]

Ever since then till now, the same idea has been promoted in the UK government, such as by advisor Professor Tim Lang of the National Health Service and the Committee on Climate Change.[130] The government is even helping farmers to go green by publishing a guide called "The Code of Good Agricultural Practice." [131]

The UK also has leaders who have adopted or advocated a plant-based diet, such as the Secretary of State for Environment, Food and Rural Affairs Hilary Benn, Member of Parliament David Drew and EU Parliament's Vice President Edward McMillan. These are good signs in the right direction and all countries could benefit from looking up at the UK's examples.

The government needs to be bold and unprecedented. I hope the UK government rises to the occasion to lead the way to save the planet. I hope UK will be a leader of the world in this. In short, any UK policy for peace, constructive aid and the compassionate, veg lifestyle, as well as green projects, are the best and the UK government can propose and/or implement many in this category.

The United States

In the United States, the Hawaiian House and Senate unanimously passed a resolution asking that vegan and vegetarian meal options to be provided in Hawaiian schools.[132]

As a part of its new climate-action plan, Cincinnati, Ohio was the first US city to encourage less meat in order to stop global warming.[133]

Government leaders are outspoken about the benefits of vegetarianism. For example, just this summer vegan US Congressman Dennis Kucinich endorsed the first-ever Vegan Earth Day in California for vegetarians and non alike.[134]

Earlier in April [2009], Senator Jamie Raskin of Maryland, USA, who had been a lifelong meat eater, initiated a vegetarian week to help the environment himself. He has stayed vegetarian ever since, and will be speaking at a national VegFest in September. Good news.[135]

[In 2009 The Baltimore City Public Schools system declared Meatless Monday.[136]]

[In April 2010, San Francisco became the first U.S. city to declare a veggie day. The San Francisco Board of Supervisors unanimously approved a resolution to support encouraging restaurants, grocery stores and schools to increase their meatless offerings on Mondays.[137]]

[The U.S. House Education and Labor Committee passed School Lunch Bill, including Organic and Vegan Pilot Programs.]

Formosa (Taiwan)

In Formosa, the president, Ma Ying-Jeou announced that eating more vegetables and less meat is one of the most important lifestyle changes people can make to lower emissions.

For a political leader to say that is truly brave and truly is a very big step. And his wife, the First Lady of Formosa, also set an example for the children by reading aloud an article, how to curb global warming, eat less meat, more vegetables and fruits as an effort to reduce emissions.

President Ma Ying-Jeou and the entire presidential office signed a declaration of measures to reduce CO_2, which includes eating locally and partaking of more vegetables and less meat.

Finally, over one-million people in Formosa (Taiwan) took a pledge to lower their meat consumption by signing their petition. [138]

V. Organic Veganism is a Spiritual Movement

Small farmers have a spiritual role in veganism as well. The vegan diet itself is a spiritual movement because it is the single most effective way to expand our human compassion and noble quality, and loving quality. It can reverse the cycle of violence and bad karmic retribution: "As we sow, so shall we reap." And it places us within a circle of love, protection and mercy from any negative happenings in the physical realm.

So, the vegan organic farmer supports countless others to have this great merit by providing them with food that has minimal, or is free of violence, and through that he surely gains many spiritual merits himself.

The Organic Vegan Lifestyle Adheres to Ahimsa (Non-Violence)

When we live and let live, when we love all beings as if we love ourselves, then that is already very highly spiritual. And, of course, that is in line with all the greatest religions on Earth. That will be very pleasing to Heaven. This allows us more to completely extend our respect and care to all life.

And that's why you feel more peaceful, you see? You feel more connected with the surroundings around you because they all pulsate with life. The Earth is pulsating with love and life, the trees, the plants, they are pulsating all this love for life. When we sit under a tree, we feel this protective love from the tree. When we enjoy a delicious fruit, we feel the connectedness of this unconditional love from the tree to offer us nutrition and a pleasing taste.

If we are in the organic, vegan trend or planting with organic, vegan farming methods, then you will feel that more and more the love from nature, the love from the planet Earth, the love from the trees, the love from even a blade of grass, from flowers. We will feel so much love in the air that we breathe. We feel so much love from the earth that we walk on. This we cannot even explain in human language. We must feel it. I always feel it, but I can't transmit this spiritual message to other people. Everyone must experience it for himself.

Once we turn to a compassionate, Heaven-intended lifestyle of a vegan diet, then we will feel more and more love, more and more connected all the time. Ahimsa means not harming any sentient beings, beginning with a vegan diet. Organic, vegan diet is the best. As we sow, so shall we reap. If we sow these benevolent seeds on the Earth, as well as in our heart, as a vegan, we avoid all animal products.

For example, most of the milk production causes suffering, first of all because the babies of the mother cows are taken away at birth. Not many people know that, including myself before. And these baby cows will soon be killed. Deprived from mother's milk and mother's love, they'll be killed as soon as they're taken away. Then, the mother is forcefully hooked up to a machine that can cause tormenting pain along with illness, just so that humans can take her milk.

Since organic, vegan farming does not use pesticides and does not have anything to do with livestock raising, milk production or any such harmful activity, it could be called a practice of compassion, in line with Heaven, with values that are echoed in many spiritual paths and religious teachings, such as the followers of Buddhism and Confucianism and as written in their scriptures.

5

IMMEDIATE GLOBAL SHIFT TO A PLANT-BASED DIET

At this point, it takes all the efforts and all the NGOs, governments, media, the public, every single individual, to get involved. Our planet is a house that is burning. If we don't work together with a united spirit to put out the fire, we will not have a home anymore. One-hundred percent of the world's people must be veg soon to save the planet.

I. THE WORLD NEEDS THE MEDIA'S NOBLE SERVICES AND LEADERSHIP

The media has a very great, heroic, noble role to save the world at this moment in our history. And while saving lives, the media also can save the loving, noble quality in human hearts as well.

The printed words are very powerful. People are too busy with their daily activities, so they look to the media for informing and reporting relevant events, important matters, and all necessary information for their lives. So, the media is a useful tool to awaken one another at this crucial time, a time when our planet and the lives on it are in danger.

I'm so glad to see many television and radio channels starting to broadcast about the urgent situation of our planet, and even the solution of the vegan diet, which is the switch that we have to make, very small change: piece of meat out, vegetarian protein in. That's it—just a small change, everyone can afford. And it's cheaper, healthier.

The media helps a lot to point people in the direction of the solution. In fact, the most urgent role of the media right now is to become vegan themselves—compassionate, noble and doing good deeds and to inform people of this urgent action. They should be an example, the media.

The media is a huge, huge help in reminding people to go in this upward direction. Encourage people through your work to become vegan, to save human lives, animal lives, and the environment. Because the vegan diet, though simple, is the giant stepping stone that would bring us higher in our evolution. Besides, time is running out for our planet. We must act fast to save lives.

Every newspaper, every day when printing out the newspaper, could just print one sentence: "Be Veg. Go Green." That's it, so easy. All the newspapers can do that. Just one headline somewhere "Be Veg, Go Green 2 Save the Planet"

I wish all the media would display a veg announcement every day on TV, newspapers, radio, etc., even on billboards, films, or movies, computer boards. Everywhere this should be the topmost concern topic.

All the media should help to save the planet because if the planet's gone, everybody'll be gone. Everybody should realize that. Money—useless, house—useless, power—useless. So we do what we can to make people realize that. We have to save the only planet that we have and the most beautiful one that we know. It's the only one we know.

Be a true, honest friend to human society: warning everyone of any harmful situation; bringing new connections and data to light, like the urgent link between meat and global warming; giving chances for people to choose a better way of life; and being a brave voice, a heroic voice especially for the voiceless, including animals who suffer so much, so much, because we are all related and affected.

The world needs the media's noble service and leadership. So please, all the courageous journalists, do what you do best: Tell the truth about how we are to save the planet.

II. Religious Leaders Guide Others in the Righteous Way of Living

The religious people and leaders should speak up about this subject, should be taking more of the leading position to help the public understand the great problem that we're facing and the solution to curb the global warming.

The religious leaders must set an example for their followers. First, of course, they must encourage their adherents to eat vegetarian, to do good and avoid evil, to encourage them to protect the environment. If religious leaders can announce to their followers to do these things, then our Earth will be guaranteed safety and will be saved, because peace begins with our plate of food. Peace begins from our dining table.

Religious leaders can give voice and strive to be a living example of the noble teachings according to their original founders, such as Jesus, Prophet Muhammad, Buddha, Guru Nanak, etc., etc., who espoused the compassionate, vegetarian lifestyle. The scriptures from the teachings of these sages all emphasize the need to care for one another and be good stewards of our Earth.

In the Christian Bible, it is said, "Meat for the belly and belly for the meat, but God will destroy both it and them." The Buddhist Mahaparinirvana Sutra also stated, "Eating meat destroys the seed of compassion and a meat eater's every action will terrify all beings due to their bodily scent of meat."

Actually, Christianity, Buddhism, Hinduism, Islam, every religion told us: Don't eat animals because they are God's creation.

The spiritual aspect of a vegetarian (vegan) diet is very clear—non-violence—"Thou shall not kill." When God said to us, "Thou shall not kill," He did not say human beings; He said all beings.

It is very clear in the Bible that we should be vegetarian (vegan). And by all scientific reasons we should be vegetarian (vegan). And by all health reasons we should be, again, vegetarian (vegan). And by all economical reasons we should be vegetarian (vegan). And by all compassionate reasons we should be vegetarian (vegan). And by saving the world we should be vegetarian (vegan).

It is stated in some research that if the people in the West would eat vegetarian (vegan) once a week, we would save 60-million people every year. So be a hero, be vegetarian (vegan), by all reasons. But why vegetarian (vegan), you would ask me. Vegetarian (vegan) is just because the God inside us wants it.

Therefore, religious adherents need to be reminded that to solve the environmental problem; we need to put these teachings into action. And the most effective action is something that citizens can do immediately—be veg. Of course, another is "go green" meaning take care of the environment and be frugal in our usage.

To be veg is living in accordance with our true religious beliefs. Forgoing meat and adopting the plant-based lifestyle means we put the principle of compassion into action.

We read it and we practice it, like nonviolence; we absolutely have to adhere to that. We don't kill and we don't steal, but we save lives and we do charity. We love each other; we help each other; and we keep to our moral standard. What doesn't belong to us we don't take. Instead we give what belong to us to those who need. All religions teach us that, so we just have to practice it.

We look back into our teaching and see what the Masters have told us, what the prophets have taught us. That's all we have to do. There's no need even to do anything else. The scriptures are really enough for us to live in peace but only if we practice it.

III. NOBLE EDUCATION TEACHES THE HEALTHY GREEN LIFESTYLE

> Our house is on fire. Our planet is in peril. You [the educators] have to inform them. You have to take immediate action. Tell them what to do. Lead them into a better life. They look upon you, they will be grateful.

INFORM THE CHILDREN

We must tell them. We must be direct and tell them honestly about what's happening to our planet in regards to global warming and let them know all the methods to prepare for it so we can reduce global warming and possibly halt it altogether.

Children's hearts are very innocent and pure; they can easily accept the guidance from the elders. Therefore, we must carefully explain to them about what is good for the planet.

After the explanation, they will understand right away and will take immediate action on what you would like them to do. It's because children have respect for the elders. But we must be a role model first.

Vegan children enjoy a happy meal of fruits, vegetables and vegan apple pie.

We are the elders; we must make an example of ourselves first, and then we can educate them because children learn from examples; they learn from shining examples more than from talking. Therefore, as adults we must be a shining example; we must do our best.

We do what is good for the planet so that the children can inherit a beautiful legacy that we leave for them. We must do whatever is necessary even if that is a huge sacrifice; but actually, we don't really need to sacrifice anything. We just need to put down that piece of meat and replace it with a piece of tofu.

MOBILIZE THE YOUNGER GENERATION

It seems that teenagers are more interested in fashion and other things rather than the urgent situation right now. But they are also often the most open-minded people. They are intelligent; they are easy; they are an impressionable and honest group of people. Once they make a connection of global warming to their lives, they may really decide to do something. You will be surprised, especially if they understand what they do can truly make a difference, they may be the first ones to take action. They just need a good leader like you.

Two very recent studies found young persons to be the ones most likely to volunteer and give of themselves.[139] This is just saying that the young persons of this age have a lot of energy and can be some of the most caring people.

So you can encourage them by helping them find active ways to show their care and love. You can also help them see how urgent global warming really is. Show them the human side of global warming, the true stories of people and animals who suffer because of this, for example, the families in island nations who have to move or plan to move, because they see the water coming to submerge their houses—or, in some cases, already did—due to the rising sea level.

Or, the inhumane treatment of animals in slaughterhouse or in cosmetic experiments—there are many films about this. We have shown them every Tuesday on the show on Supreme Master Television called "Stop Animal

Cruelty." This is unimaginable cruelty. This is beyond human, moral standards. It is below our dignity to treat animals this way. So, if you show them some of this truth about how animals suffer for humans' palate, you will awaken in the students their compassionate nature, and they will decide to do something about it.

Or, you can show also how the migrating birds have to fly farther and farther to find a place to nest, and the polar bears swim longer and longer now because there is no more ice until sometimes they drown of exhaustion, or why the neighboring country has so many floods in recent years, so many disasters, etc., etc.

Tell them how climate change is affecting real lives, real animals, real people and their own lives as well. Then, the young ones will realize that halting climate change comes before all else, everything that is important to them in this world, even before job, before money, and even before having fun, because without a stable climate and a living planet, no one would be able to enjoy the things that we want to enjoy or get to do the things that we want to do.

But it's also important to show the young people that there is still hope; we can still save the planet. You can tell them this: It's a chance that they can be true heroes, by being vegan and spread the news of this solution. They can save lives, including their own, and also of people all over the world and countless animal lives around the world.

If you explain all the benefits of being vegan—for personal, for the animals, for the hungry people, for the starving children—they will love it and they will be so excited because they know they can really make a difference.

The young people are oftentimes the most ready to change their lifestyle if they see a reason for it. Their age group is also, in many cases, the first one to see that vegetarianism is good, is correct. So, I think if we explain to them logically how it is the most important action to solve global warming, they will be motivated. They will support you. They will be behind you. They will do it.

HELP TO INITIATE VEGAN SCHOOL LUNCHES

There are many studies now that show the benefits of a healthy school lunch and snacks program. Children are even known to concentrate better when they are eating more fresh fruits and vegetables.

The Americans' First Lady now always introduces fresh fruits and vegetables to the children of America. And if we help the school to understand these benefits, they may also adopt them more widely themselves. Nowadays, many schools and parents even plant vegetables in the school or in the home gardens with the children, and the children love these activities as well, as they're eating more vegetables—which they grew themselves!

We can also tell our children that by being vegan, they are directly helping to heal and save our planet, helping the parents, and helping themselves and all the lives in this world. Children are very loving at heart. So, if they know that by being vegan they can save many lives, they would be very, very willing to do it. We want to be able to leave a world for the children, a world of green and lush beauty, a world of humans and animals peacefully coexisting together. They will love to help to make this happen.

IV. NGOS PROMOTE THE VEGAN MOVEMENT

The best way for NGOs to help is if all of you actively, together, encourage the number one solution, and the most effective —that is, the vegan diet—to halt global warming, because we don't have much time now to wait for the green technology to even take effect. Even then, the green technology also takes more time even to install.

So the veg diet is the number one [solution] because the meat industry emits the most heat-trapping greenhouse gas for our planet, and pollution even—more than 50%.[140] Imagine if we eliminate more than 50% of harmful gas, and then our planet at least cools off more than 50% almost immediately.

If we go into organic farming methods, all the tillable land on the planet, if we use it all for organic farming, then that in turn also absorbs 40% of the CO_2 in the atmosphere as well.[141] So altogether combine this, we will cool the planet in no time. This is not anything mysterious or superstitious; it is all scientific. It's all proven and it's all clear.

So, it is you and your talents to organize, inform and speak out that I rely on to get the governments' attention at the Copenhagen climate change meeting. Please do your best. And the government can further amplify this solution after hearing you out.

The NGOs know well how to start the constructive movements in the world. They are very, very essential and very important to our planet. All the NGOs are very, very important to humanity and to our survival as well once they start the action. And at this point, it takes all the efforts and all the NGOs, governments, media, the public, every single individual, to get involved.

Our planet is a house that is burning. If we don't work together with a united spirit to put out the fire, we will not have a home anymore. One-hundred percent of the world's people must be veg soon to save the planet.

We can keep the emission goals, but must expand them and prioritize them wisely. First and foremost, eliminate the single largest source of human-caused methane; namely, livestock. Stop animal production, then we will stop global warming—very simple, because global warming is caused by animal products. That's it, very simple, straightforward, nothing mysterious, nothing difficult.

To be honest, as the plans are going right now, we can't save the planet. It will be too late the way we are doing now; it will be too late to save our world. So we have to be veg first and that is also to go green at the same time. And then any other green technology, we will have time to develop and install.

And even a heavenly world we will have because being veg changes everything drastically, from the environment to people's mentality, to the standard of our world and to having peace in the world, to eliminate hunger, to have brotherhood truly for humankind.

With temperatures stabilized, ecosystems balanced, animals thriving in peace and humans finding new health and happiness and incredible new inventions, our life will become a dreamlike Heaven as never imagined before.

Supreme Master Ching Hai International Association Members promoting the vegan solution during COP15 in Copenhagen, Denmark, 2009.

V. Be the Change You Want to See

Change the World by Changing Ourselves

The best to save the planet is the individual.

It begins with us. Since time immemorial, evolution always begins with the individual. If we want to change the world, we change ourselves first. Now, even if the government forbids smoking or drinking or drugs, but if people individually continue, then we have not made much difference. So now, we have to change.

The more people who eliminate meat and, indeed, all animal products from their lives, the more we have a chance to save the planet and not only that, to actually restore our earthly home to her original grace and beauty and even more so, more than what we have known, more beautiful, more abundant, more peace, more gladness than what we have known up to now.

And there will be more incredible inventions to come if our Earth restores itself, leading a life of compassionate, merciful and peaceful existence with all beings on this planet.

Positive Energy Will Save the World

All of you out there, please continue. Do your work because everybody's effort really counts. Even one flyer of information about the meat diet and about the benefit of the vegetarian diet to help the planet does count. Even one word does count. One piece of information does count. Everybody helps a little bit, and then the whole planet will change because of the collective consciousness of the positive direction.

Everybody wants the same thing; everybody wants to save the planet; everybody wants to sustain the globe, to keep this way of life, or even better. Then the consciousness is huge. The energy is very benevolent. And if everybody just puts down that piece of meat, changes the lifestyle—very simple.

> Save the planet first and things will change after. It's not you alone can save the planet. It's the people who change their consciousness. If they go veg, go green, do good, then that means they have changed for the better. Their consciousness has gone up a higher level, and then of course, they merit the Earth. They could continue to live here and their children, grandchildren, great-grandchildren, etc.

At that time people will be in a higher level of consciousness and things will be clearer to them and to all. We will live in peace and love. You have to envision a positive world, the Heaven on Earth that you would like it to be. You have to envision the nobler world, the positive world, the beautiful world, the Heaven world. Saving the world is a compassionate act. Even if the world is not saved, you are. You are saved by your loving kindness. Your merit will be multi-fold because you want to save others.

If you want to save the world, if you want to do anything toward this goal, you're enlarging your nobility, your heavenly attribute. So if you spread the encouragement to save the planet, if you go veg, if you go green, if you do good deeds, you help others because you want to save the lives of other beings on Earth, then you have a saintly quality. You reawaken your holiness. It's not just about saving the physical planet and the physical lives. It's also about how great you are for wanting to do so and actually partaking in this life-saving crusade.

The Power is in the Consumers' Hands

No one can prevent us from doing what's right for our lives and that of our planet. We just stop using, eating, buying animal products, then these corporations will just disappear in no time. So, the power is in our hands.

We, the ordinary consumers, exercise the most powerful vote simply by boycotting meat, and all the animal products, and becoming vegans. There would be no need to continue the life-threatening practice of animal raising if we all became vegan.

The pork industry in the US has lost US$5.4 billion since 2007 [as of 2009].[142] Company after major company is declaring bankruptcy right now, so they're asking for help from the government, which ended up buying their unwanted pork products from the farmers for US$105 million in 2009.[143] The reasons that the powerful pork industry is struggling are, number one, high costs of feed grains, and number two, the consumers are not buying their products as much anymore since the swine flu outbreak. Imagine if no one eats meat, no one would ever kill these animals for a living. That would be more powerful than the companies' lobbying.

We have the power. The animal companies only have power because we give them the power! We share our power with them. But if we stop buying it, they're gone.

Supreme Master Ching Hai's "How to Veg 4 Starters"

1. Veg before you shop—means eating vegan food before you shop, so you don't feel hungry when you are in the supermarket.
2. Go straight to the veg section of the supermarket.
3. Get veg recipes from the Internet or from friends, or from a vegan organization.
4. Make supportive, new, veg friends.
5. Get info about veg benefits.
6. Spread the veg trend.
7. Feel like a saint.

BE GREEN

Be green. These are actions to protect the environment such as planting trees, developing sustainable energy and driving hybrid cars, etc. Of course, this includes the green diet, the vegan diet.[144]

Support Organic Vegan Farming

Try to be organic. Buy organic food to support organic farmers. Do anything you can to support this organic, vegetarian farming.

Livestock farmers who chose to go into the vegan or organic vegan business, from the US to Iran to Au Lac (Vietnam) to Formosa (Taiwan), they changed because they had gotten new information, sometimes from other people, that there are better ways to be a farmer, a true farmer, who grows life-sustaining products and works in harmony with the land. We, too, can be the ones who inform, who talk to the animal farmers, one by one, about the harms of meat and the benefits of organic vegan.

Whoever wants to do it, whoever can, do it. Go to the farmers, talk to them. Whenever you can, make the time to go. Even though we are not in a power position like the government, but we can try, one by one. Tell them the picture. Tell them the situation. Tell them again and again until they understand. Write to them. Talk to them. We can only try our best.

Plant Trees and Vegetables

We could plant organic vegetables and trees. Better still are those fruit trees and nut trees, and those vegetables or legumes like beans and stuff that need little water.

One tree at a time, and then we will never have an oxygen shortage.

You can plant vegetables or trees on your land or around your home. Fruits can fill us up as well. I am not referring to those sweet fruits only. There are many different kinds of fruits, including cucumbers, watermelons, white gourd, ridged gourds and papaya. Plant whatever you can. Plant the ones that can grow easily, are filling and nutritious, grow fast, and don't need too much water, because we can live on anything.

For people who have a yard, instead of growing grass or something else, or let it be vacant, grow vegetables. You can grow enough for yourselves or as a supplement. This way, you can have good, vegetarian food, save money, time and the energy used on transportation.

You can even plant and harvest indoors. Or if we have a balcony, we can even plant it in water. We must start now so that you can have your own vegetables.

If there is a water shortage, you can plant more beans or fruits. Beans are very easy to grow. They grow very fast. They can grow without water. You can learn how to grow things by watching Supreme Master TV.[145]

Be Frugal

Live a simple life, more simple, the more simple the better.

Be frugal, meaning don't use more than what we need and appreciate what we have. The resources nature has given to us are precious and limited. We can't abuse it because only when we spend wisely will they last.

We don't have to always buy new and fashionable clothes. We don't have to go to the latest restaurant trend. There are many things in life which could give us joy and satisfaction without much of the money involved. We can always live on without furniture; it's also fine.

You save—you use less hot water, shower less time, and don't keep water running while you're showering, don't keep water running while you're brushing your teeth, turn off your computer, turn off the light when you don't need it, turn off anything standing by that you don't need, then you will save maybe 10% of your bills, water and electricity together.

Another way to cultivate simplicity is to spend time also in the tranquility of nature, or create a natural environment at home where we can go for peace and quiet. Reading mind-uplifting books such as spiritual scriptures, as well as practicing meditation, are also good ways to remind ourselves that we truly don't need much to be happy and live a contented, peaceful life.

Do Good Deeds

We have to create the loving atmosphere for our planet.
This will also help protect us.

Another good way to quicken our movement to a sustainable planet is to generate more positive energy: Do good deeds and be loving and kind. Expand our loving quality. This is what will create a shield, invincible, to protect us and the planet.

We should do good deeds to further strengthen the loving, positive atmosphere of our planet. We have to create a happy, loving atmosphere for our planet, then we can live in that atmosphere, be protected and be happy. This is very scientific. We don't need even to believe in any religions to understand this: We create our atmosphere. If everyone creates the harmonious atmosphere, our planet will be in peace, and we will be like in paradise.

If you have spare money or Buddhas and Bodhisattvas have given you more than you need, then go give to the needy and the poor. You give only when someone is in need. You shouldn't give for merits.

PRAY AND REPENT

Pray, pray fervently. Pray to Heaven, to all the Buddhas, to gods, to all the angels who are helping to awaken us. Pray to all the animals that we have harmed and tortured directly or indirectly by consuming meat—pray for their forgiveness. Pray for Heaven's protection and forgiveness as well. Pray all the gods to help awaken us on time to save our home. We have to pray sincerely and act swiftly. We truly cannot do this by ourselves alone.

We must repent for all the harm done to the Earth and her inhabitants and ask again and again for forgiveness. And we have to reverse our action. And the best way to repent is to make an effort to change. Turn around, do what is good. Refrain from all what is bad.

We can pray that divine power manifests on Earth to awaken leaders, media, influential people, and all the world citizens to take the right steps to preserve our planet, and fast—fast before it's too late. Because at this point, we do need Heaven's intervention to save our planet, not to pray to them to protect us; just to pray so that they awaken everybody to the solution of the vegan diet, because that is the solution that will save our planet.

START THE VEGAN TREND

Spread the News

As ones who have helped to awaken countless people to the reality so that they can change their lifestyle for the better, these are the true pioneers of their fields and rightful stars and heroes of our time.

We have to spread the news; everyone else who cares about the planet must spread the news. Then people will join us.

Write to Governments and the Media

For a farther-reaching effect, you can contact government officials by writing and letting them know the facts about this dire global situation, with all the information available on our website [SupremeMasterTV.com] for you to download and copy and send.[146]

The government is aware. It is just perhaps the government is putting priority elsewhere. So, if you and other citizens are concerned, you could contact your government and write to them, inform them or remind them of the urgency of the situation that we and our future generations are facing.

Write to your government leaders about the veg solution, go and visit with them, if that it possible. For leaders, they are aware of these grave problems facing their countries. Now, if the citizens also support them, remind them that they're concerned and that this is for their best interests, then they will be even more energized to address climate change. Then they will remember that global warming is the most important agenda, that it's their duty not only professionally, but also personally, because it affects themselves and their children as well.

Write to the whole government, not just the president, because the president alone sometimes cannot easily make the decision. Write to whichever departments of the government you can. Everyone does it together. And then make many copies and send one each to the president, and the key departments for making the decision.

Write a lot. Email to them, fax to them, write to them. Write to newspapers. Talk to radio. Talk to TV. Do interviews. Tell everybody you know. Try lobbying where you can. Talk to the leaders that you know. Talk to their friends, if you cannot know the leader, you talk to the leader's friend, the leader's family, the leader's acquaintance, the leader's waiter, waitress, housekeepers, cleaners, drivers, their family members, their children, the children who go to the same school as your children, their employees, their secretary, whoever you think can reach the leaders' ears in an acceptable way.

Should the leaders take some positive steps, then we should write to thank them also and encourage them. We should have positive encouragement. We have to encourage them when they do some right things and so they go further in that direction, or even better, improve.

I wrote a letter to President Obama, I wrote a letter to the European Parliament, European Commissioner, and they answered me. They say they will take heed, take notice of what I said and my words, my advice, will be in their heart, in their mind, in the days ahead. I appreciate these kinds of leaders who do listen.

Lead Grassroots Movements and the Vegan Trend

Hold grassroots seminars. Offer evidence and information to the public about the solution to global warming. Join efforts with other vegetarians. By all working together, the fruits of labor are multiplied and the planet can be saved.

As individuals and communities, we must take action instead of waiting for the government or the technology to be developed. It's so simple. Just one solution: the compassionate diet, because compassion begets compassion. That's a very simple law of the universe. Every action has a reaction. So, no need to wait for government policy approval process or financial resources and so on.

On a more local level again, you can sponsor a cooking class. This will help people understand just how easy it is to cook delicious and nutritious veg meals for themselves and their families.

I also had the idea of a chain of vegan restaurants that would serve fast, tasty, nutritious vegan dishes called Loving Hut; and it did come to fruition. There are many of them now. More than 90 [updated number: 138], in many different countries, Loving Hut restaurants are opened, from Formosa (Taiwan) to France to the United States to Australia.[147] They open in busy places like shopping centers and main intersections.

One of Supreme Master Ching Hai's delicious vegan dishes featured on her special cooking show "A Gift of Love" SupremeMasterTV.com/gol; SupremeMasterTV.com/veg

People can open vegan restaurants also, everyone. They don't go for it necessarily because it's vegan, but because they really think it's just normal, great food or as the customers, young and old report, "Even better than meat!" So, by making vegan cuisine and products more accessible to people, it becomes a real alternative.

Loving Hut, the fastest-growing international vegan restaurant chain inspired by Supreme Master Ching Hai wins VegNews Magazine's 2010 Veggie Awards in the category: Favorite Restaurant (worldwide)

People are trying to unite now to solve this urgent crisis. I see improvement and acceptance everywhere.

I see peace efforts, I see generous helping hands from all nations and individuals and groups and organizations.

I see love growing in different ways.

These signs might be still insignificant now, but they are like the sparks of fire, that will soon turn to mighty flames, that will cinder past ignorance and hatred, and making a new beginning of a nobler and saintlier race on Earth.

Please think positive and keep doing what you can to awaken our neighbors. And keep dreaming of a heavenly world in our lifetime and continue to the next generations to come.

We are together. We are fearless. We are strong. We are determined to change the world. We are courageous. We are with all humanity who wish for a peaceful, safe, loving world.

And we all deserve it! Please continue.

6

HUMANITY'S LEAP INTO THE GOLDEN ERA

The time has come for us to change, evolve, grow and stand tall as the rightful crown of creation, the benevolent rulers and protectors, and Heaven's children on Earth. Together, let us make the unprecedented leap to the Golden Era, to the time of compassion, harmony, kindness and true peace that awaits us. I know that we can do it.

I. A TURNING POINT IN HUMAN EVOLUTION

You see, one small step from everyone in the right direction can result in a big leap in our evolution as a human race. And that small step is very simple. It's just: no killing. Abiding by the principle of "Live and let live," adhering to the universal law where we grant life to beget life. Because like attracts like; that we all know. This, of course, includes adopting a vegan diet.

Humans are naturally more generous and peaceful in their heart; it's just that we all have been misinformed, misunderstood for a long, long, long time. We thought meat was good for us, we thought dairy was good for us, we thought fish was good for us, we thought eggs were good for us. It's all wrong. It's all the opposite. It all has been proven that these things that we have been told that are good for us—like meat, fish, dairy, eggs, whatever animal products are "good for us"—is all wrong. It's the opposite of what is good. It has been bringing us suffering, sickness and tremendous loss of finances from tax payers for curing disease and related business.

So, we have been misled, for a long, long time. Now, we have to do research. We have to listen to the wise doctors and scientists. We have to see the result of their research: that meat and animal products are really, really poisonous for us. We have to stop now, especially stop for our children's sake. We can't keep poisoning our children anymore; they are helpless. The poor children, they rely on us, they think we know better, but it's not our fault either. We just need to turn around.

Why it's not our fault? Because we have also been taught that way. And our grandparents, our great-grandparents have also been taught that way. And for being too busy, too busy for daily survival, working, we have no time to do research, so we did not know that these things are truly poisonous to us.

And above all, it is eating up our planet. It's not just killing people, it's not just killing animals, it's killing our planet. And we have to stop it in order to save our world. We just turn around, that's it. Just walk the opposite way, the right way without causing anymore suffering; no taking more lives, but loving and protecting all creatures. That's the leap that all humanity needs.

We will feel completely different after we make this leap. We will feel evolved to the higher level of consciousness automatically. Just imagine we are big, strong, intelligent and able. We are able to plant all kinds of stuff to eat, and we should not use our might, our intelligence, our capability, to harass, to molest, to torture, to cause suffering and to murder those little, helpless, innocent animals who have never done us any harm. According to the law, they are innocent. And if we kill innocent beings, we are the ones who should be punished. I am sorry if I offend you, but this is the truth. And I am sure you understand it.

Through our leap in this evolution, we can leave this existence of want and fear, toward a true life of peace and love and enlightenment —from the vicious cycle of killing, suffering, and violence to a circle of loving kindness, protection, and happiness.

Can we imagine a world where the meek ones never have to fear the strong, where there is no more violence, no fighting among neighbors near or far, and no child has to die of hunger, thirst or illness every few seconds, every day, while their mother watches, completely helpless with her heart drowning in sorrow?

As I am speaking, many children are dying somewhere. Every few seconds, a child dies of hunger. We cannot keep doing this. We cannot wait longer. We have to save these lives—not just the lives of animals, but the lives of our children, even if it's not our children, other people's children.

Meat causes so much suffering because it causes hunger and war. We use up all our cereals, grain, soy and good resources, and land and water to support the meat industry, and therefore the world is short of food and water. So, in order to save lives we have to stop the meat industry.

The way we are living right now is a deeply degraded condition of what we really are. We are the children of God, which is all loving and kindness. We are the heirs of Heaven. We've just forgotten. Can you imagine a God who comes here to Earth and kills everything in sight to eat? Sorry, if there is a God like that, I don't want to be Hiers child. Would you like to be the children of that kind of God?

Okay, no. Thank you. Thank you. You are so kind. Now, if God is all merciful, all compassion, all loving and we are the children of God, then don't you think we should walk like God's children on Earth?

We have to walk the way of love and compassion. We have to represent our Father if we want to glorify His name. We always pray every day, "Hallowed be thy name in Heaven as well as on Earth," but what do we do to hallow Hiers name? We have to represent Hirm.

We always pray to God because we believe God is merciful, protective, compassionate and loving. And we are the children of God; we must represent these qualities. We are those qualities: We are loving and kindness. We have just been misled, misinformed, and we have forgotten. So please just remember. These qualities are deep inside us, so we know there must be something better than what we see around us.

We do have examples through our history of human beings whose lives were so uplifting that they continue to shine until today—not only spiritual teachers, but philosophers like Plato, statesmen like Socrates, the mathematician Pythagoras and the poet Ralph Waldo Emerson of America. They were all vegetarian. Are you surprised? No, you are not. You don't look surprised to me. So you knew all that. All the great people, they are vegetarian or vegan. So, if we study them carefully, we will see that at the basic core of the civilized life they taught is the vegan diet.

The vegan diet is one of the first, single, greatest acts of compassion, of not harming another life and not damaging the environment even. If we compare a meat-based diet to a vegan diet, [the meat-based diet] takes around 14 times as much water, six times as much grain, 10 times as much energy, and over 20 times as much land, while often destroying precious rainforest.

Being vegan is good business in terms of virtuous merit, as well as preserving the only home we have. The less damage and harm we inflict upon the planet and her inhabitants, the less we have to pay. We are paying dearly now, and we will pay much dearer if we don't stop the meat/animal industry.

The more we exert our loving kindness and protection towards all beings, the greater we will be in the world, the greater will be the feeling in our heart as well as in the Kingdom of Heaven. That's why great Masters and other illuminated souls of the past all taught us, one and the same, that if we don't wish to be harmed, we must not impose harm on others. You look in all religions, [and] all say the same, this sentence, this same meaning. Whatever is good for us, we should do for others; that whatever we sow, we will reap, without fail. That's why they did teach us not to eat animals and to be vegan.

If we make this leap, a very small change in the diet; instead of meat, instead of animal protein, we choose vegetable protein, which is first class anyway. Animal protein is second class, why? Because they have eaten the first-class vegetables and fruit and then we eat their flesh. That is second class. We are humans, why do we choose the second-class stuff? It doesn't befit us. So we have to make this leap.

We have to make this leap, ladies and gentleman, because if we do, the Golden Era will be here in no time, heralding a time of peaceful living without the perpetual loss of lives—early deaths in the tens of billions each year! Tortured and murdered for our fleeting pleasure, which we could always replace. Meat is replaceable.

There are so many wonders of earthly life that we have yet to experience and discover, so much scientific knowledge to be revealed and explored, and invented, and incredible technologies to be discovered and developed! There are better social systems. These are things mostly beyond our present level of logic or even our imagination, but they can only be achieved through tapping into our wisdom and creative power.

In order to open this wisdom, we must first remove the harmful, obstructive substances that block and suppress it, like meat, dairy, fish, poultry and all animal products. These things obstruct our intelligence, delay our progress, not just spiritually, morally but technologically as well.

Finally, besides our personal reasons of wanting to welcome a golden era, we also have the planet to consider, which as I'm sure you know, we are at risk of losing anytime now. So, this leap in consciousness is also to save our planet and all other beings that deserve a harmonious world to live in.

If everyone makes this leap or shift, we can save our planet. I promise, with all the honor that I have, and God be witness. At the same time, we elevate ourselves, which has been long, long overdue.

THE HUMAN RACE IS READY TO ADVANCE

It's high time that the human race should rise to a higher level of consciousness. They should be noble, kind and compassionate. Go veg, be green, do good, is not just for the planet, it's for the whole human race ennobling, spiritual merit and quality. They should do it, just for the sake of being noble.

We have to turn back to our caring and compassionate nature inside our heart. That's very simple. We are that. We are compassion. We are merciful; we are caring.

If we truly wish to see real harmony born between humans and animals and nature and Heaven, we must be the harmony, we must live in harmony and act also in harmony, which includes the act of eating harmoniously each time we come to the table.

Making a vegan choice is thus a true advancement in the evolution and goodness of our humanity. And then we also know that like attracts like, goodness attracts more goodness. As we share this compassionate truth with others, not only will our own humanity be further uplifted, so will the world's.

II. The Earth is Ascending to the Higher Galactic Civilization

Concerning the ascending of our planet, that is the universal plan for our planet that we should catch up, that we should ascend with other higher, spiritually developed planets. That is the plan. But the humans are given free will, and for that free will, they have not been using it wisely.

Learn from the Lessons of Mars and Venus

Earth merging with other [planets] in the galaxy—that's a big vision. We only need to look at our own neighboring planets, Mars and Venus, to see that the vision is bleak, is disastrous, if we don't make the right choice, the right change now.

Any planetary scientist knows that Mars and Venus went through dramatic atmospheric changes in the past, similar to what we have begun to experience right now. Long ago, Mars and Venus were once a lot like our planet—they had water, life and people similar to us. But the inhabitants of Mars and Venus destroyed their respective planetary homes because they raised too much livestock, and the gases released triggered an irreversible greenhouse-gas effect, plus poisonous hydrogen sulfide in the case of Mars. So, that's why we see only the traces of the landforms and oceans that once used to be there.

Around five-billion planets have been destroyed or in similar fate as Venus or Mars. Only those planets that have inhabitants with a low level of consciousness have been destroyed or ruined, not the high level ones.

And on Venus, the atmosphere is so heated and choked up with CO_2—carbon dioxide—scientists thus called it "runaway global warming," and say this is what the future of Earth might be like.

The planets that were saved from destruction, like Venus, were saved because their societies became vegan —I mean the ones that are saved. I mentioned there were four Venuses—only two of them were saved because their societies became vegan. The other two Venuses were destroyed —one is completely gone, one is boiling hot, uninhabitable, because they have not been vegan.

Most of the people on Mars did not know, or did not listen that the veg diet was the solution. The Martians went through destruction once and never forgot the painful lesson, and they were kind enough to send their message for Earth's humans through our contact. Their message is: Be virtuous, save your home before it is too late.

We are near there; we are almost at the point of no return. That is why we continuously try right now to spread the solution message: vegetarian diet. It offers physical power to stop the global warming because it has a moral power. It has a scientific power, like, "Like attracts like." We have to respect life, and then we will beget life.

NOBLE FRIENDS IN THE GALAXIES ARE WAITING

As many as non-vegetarian planets, there are also as many vegetarian planets. It's countless, countless. In our galaxy alone, they're countless already. And these vegetarian-society planets, they're more advanced than us. They even have traveling belts. There are much more that we could never dream of.

These people in those societies, they can enjoy a lot of time for their leisure, and develop their hobbies and their talents, and discover their dormant capabilities as well. Therefore, in such a society, there are many wonderful inventions have been born. And many wonderful things happen because people are relaxed and do what they do best. No one ever worries about lacking physical necessities, so their lives are full of freedom and happiness. Doesn't that sound wonderful?

All such societies are also vegan, I told you. Their concept of life is very clear—very clear, very selfless, unconditional, very intelligent. I have not seen a single civilization so advanced and happy, joyful that is not a vegan society.

Also, once we stop the killing, then we will generate a more loving, kind and inviting atmosphere for other noble beings in the galaxy to perhaps join us or be in contact with us.

If, somehow, we have the fortune to know this kind of planet, or this kind of developed being, then the happiness and peace of that planet or of those people will make us feel such an ache to be there, and not care so much for the gain and blame of this world. We will just leave this world anytime if we have a chance to join them. But as we are not as developed as they are —spiritually, mentally and psychologically and virtue-wise—some of us are not, so we cannot be so close to them, nor that we cannot join them, nor that our planet could be ranked as one of them.

So they are waiting eagerly. They've been transmitting messages to us that we should develop more so that we can catch up with the whole galaxy system, and that they're always standing by to help us to elevate our level of spiritual understanding, mental capability as well as technology.

They will not force their will upon us either. They are waiting, waiting and waiting for us to be ready. So long as we do not choose to live according to high universal standards, we will have difficulty in finding peace within ourselves, much more so with other beings in the universe. We will be out of touch with our neighboring planets' citizens, thus, we do not know their existence.

However, it's not difficult to change all this. We will just have to return to our original, loving self because that's what we are. We are love. We are divine. We are compassion. We are all the best in the universe. It's just we forget.

III. Realizing the Eden Dream

If the world were to go 100% vegetarian right now, the good effect of it would be seen within more or less 60 days. That is eight weeks. Within eight weeks we would see immediate effect. Of course, you'll also see immediately, it's almost immediately. But to see the whole, big picture, you can realize it within eight weeks, eight short weeks.

Within eight weeks all disasters will stop. That's how Heaven is created. What do you think? Where does Heaven come from? Heaven is a place where all beings act in the same way. I mean, not like uniformly, but in the same level of compassion, same level of love and same level of spiritual knowledge, understanding, same level of nobility. That's what Heaven is.

Heaven does come down to meet us if we are walking up to meet Heaven's standard. And if everyone could realize this and walk the baby steps, actually only one step, one very important step that decides the fate of our planet, that is the vegetarian step, everything else will come to us unasked. If we are merciful, we will beget mercy. The universal law never fails.

The negative, murderous, bad energy will change into benevolent, happy, relaxing, benevolent to all of the inhabitants of this planet, including to animals, and of course, foremost the humans.

And what kind of Earth would we live in? It would be Eden again. We will have sudden peace and sudden realization of sameness between all nations, between all humans and between humans and animals. The realization will dawn upon us. There's no need explanation. People will suddenly understand that we're all equal. We and all co-inhabitants, animals alike, are equal. And people will have respect even for trees and plants.

If we change our lifestyle to a more heavenly quality, then the heavenly intelligence will be awakened again within us and then we will have an endless list of inventions and convenience at our fingertips. We will have flying car, I mean, not just the way they do it now, but more conveniently. We might even have just flying belt like other planets.

Our scientific and technological understanding will also go beyond Earth. Because with an elevated, compassionate atmosphere, we can even communicate with other more advanced planet people, and learn from them, exchange with them our knowledge and their knowledge.

Each nation would naturally have sufficient resources and wholeheartedly exchange help to each other. There are systems like that that exist without money, based on what I have seen in more highly developed societies in the universe, such as on other planets. It's not the system, this or that. It's the people, the concept of life, the concept of the society has to change first, the people's concept. Once they make a switch to change into a more sociable, more neighborly, more global family-like, then that kind of exchanging system will automatically come to realization.

Everyone will love and share with each other: love, affection and possessions. And then we will have a happier life, less unfortunate people, less or no homeless people, less or no hungry kids, less or no disease at all. And animals will be protected: no more flesh eaters, only vegetarians or vegan.

You will greet each other with a smile every day and no competitiveness in their work; everyone leaves everyone alone, just love and friendship. And the higher the consciousness of a planet, the more intensive of that kind of energy, loving and kindness.

> Being vegan worldwide is the advancement of compassion that will uplift and unify all cultures, bringing tranquility to humans and animals alike. The inner peace that comes from replacing killing with respect for all life will spread like a wave across the globe, elevate human hearts and create a harmonious Eden on Earth. That will bring us all to a lasting Golden Era.

Supreme Master Ching Hai in Monaco, 2007

APPENDICES

1. Sea-Level Rise and its Worldwide Effects

It is not only the small, island states that need to worry about sea-level rise. More than 70 percent of the world's population lives on coastal plains, and 11 of the world's 15 largest cities are on the coastal estuaries. Over the 20th century, sea levels rose between 10 and 20 centimeters (4-8 inches).

The IPCC puts predictions of 21st century sea-level rise at nine to 88 cm. **Even this comparatively modest projected sea-level rise will wreak havoc.** Coastal flooding and storm damage, eroding shorelines, salt water contamination of fresh water supplies, flooding of coastal wetlands and barrier islands, and an increase in the salinity of estuaries are all realities of even a small amount of sea-level rise.

One frighteningly real possibility is the melting of Greenland's ice sheet. According to the IPCC, "Climate models indicate that the local warming over Greenland is likely to be one to three times the global average. Ice-sheet models project that a local warming of larger than 3°C [5.4°F], if sustained for millennia, would lead to virtually a complete melting of the Greenland ice sheet with a resulting sea-level rise of about 7 m" (*IPCC 3rd Assessment, Synthesis Report, Summary for Policy Makers).*

Between the Greenland ice sheet and the Western Antarctic ice sheet the world could well be facing a 13-meter (43-foot) rise in sea level if we do not drastically curb our greenhouse gas emissions. Even a small fraction of this much sea-level rise would be an economic and humanitarian disaster. The following are possible consequences of rising sea levels:

- **Billions spent on adaptation**—if you can afford it. A recent study estimated the costs of adapting to even a one-meter sea-level rise in the US would amount to US$156 billion (3% of the GNP).
- With only a one-meter sea-level rise some island nations, such as the Maldives, would be submerged. Already, two of the islands that make up Kiribati (a Pacific island nation) have gone under the waves. **If current warming trends continue, cities like London, Bangkok and New York will end up below sea level,** displacing millions and causing massive economic damage.
- Rising oceans will contaminate both surface and underground fresh water supplies, worsening the world's existing fresh water shortage.

- Rural populations and farmland (especially rice) on some coasts will be wiped out. (Source: http://www.greenpeace.org/international/campaigns/climate-change/ impacts/sea_level_rise/)

2. **More Global Glacial Retreat**

   - The snow pack from the Sierra Nevada Mountains, U.S.A., which provides irrigation water to California's Central Valley, the world's fruit and vegetable basket, is already melting earlier in the spring and is projected to decrease by 30-70 percent by the end of the century. (Source: http://www.sierranevadaalliance.org/ programs/db/pics/1133215435_14399.f_pdf.pdf Sierra Climate Change Toolkit 2nd edition, Sierra Nevada Alliance)
   - Ice fields on Africa's highest mountain, Kilimanjaro, shrank by 80% over the past century, with a 33% decrease from 1989 to 2000 alone. (Source: Thompson LG, Mosley-Thompson E, Davis ME, Henderson KA, Brecher HH, Zagorodnov VS, Mashiotta TA, Lin PN, Mikhalenko VN, Hardy DR, Beer J. 2002. "Kilimanjaro ice core records: evidence of Holocene climate change in tropical Africa". Science 298: 589—593.http://bprc.osu.edu/Icecore/589.pdf
   - Global warming makes China's glaciers shrink by 7% a year, which could have devastating effects on the 300 million who depend on them for water. (Source: "Ice-capped Roof Of World Turns To Desert" By Geoffrey Lean 08 May 2006, The Independent, http://www.countercurrents.org/cc-lean080506.htm)
   - Since the 1930s glacial areas in the mountains of Central Asia have shrunk 35-50 percent and hundreds of small glaciers have already vanished. (Source: http://www.unep.org/pdf/ABCSummaryFinal.pdf UNEP Atmospheric Brown Clouds: Regional Assessment Report With Focus on Asia 2008)

3. **Extreme Global Weather Conditions**

2010 is the hottest year on record thus far:

This year is on track to being the hottest in recorded history, according to climate scientists at the US National Oceanographic and Atmospheric Administration (NOAA).

With July temperatures being the second highest in history, those during the months of March, April, May and June were the highest on record.

In June 2010 David Easterling of NOAA's National Climatic Data Center also noted the unusual finding that land masses across the entire globe were warm.

Moreover, 17 countries, comprising 19% of the Earth's total land area and including northern nations such as Finland and Russia, have set new records for most oppressive heat.

This is the largest surface area on the planet to have experienced such unprecedented high temperatures in the same year. Regarding these alarming figures, Dr. Mark Serreze, Director of the US National Snow and Ice Data Center states, "The point of the matter is that global warming has not stopped."

Kevin Trenberth, head of the climate analysis section at the US National Center for Atmospheric Research (NCAR), further warned that in such conditions we should prepare for increased tropical storms, saying, "The last time it was this warm was when we had the record-breaking hurricane season that led to Katrina and Rita, and we ran out of alphabet (characters). This year the temperatures in the Atlantic are higher than they were in 2005."

(Source: http://solveclimatenews.com/news/20100816/most-ever-heat-record-temperatures-19-percent-earths-surface
http://news.discovery.com/earth/heat-record-climate-change.html
http://www.washingtonpost.com/wp-dyn/content/
article/2010/08/13/AR2010081306090.html
http://www.accuweather.com/blogs/news/story/35632/hottest-year-on-record-so-far.asp
http://green.blogs.nytimes.com/2010/08/17
weather-extremes-and-climate-change)

In Russia

In 2010, the extreme heat in Russia led to 14,340 deaths in Moscow in July alone. The heat also caused the worst drought conditions in European Russia in a half century, prompting the Russian government to suspend wheat exports. The heat, in turn, caused extreme fire danger over most of European Russia.

(Source: http://climateprogress.org/2010/08/07/russian-heat-wave-drought-soil-moisture-wheat)

In the U.S.

The year 2010 began with freezing conditions in Florida. Then it became the hottest summer on record for the region.

In Australia

Northern Australia had the wettest May-October ever recorded, while the southwestern part had its driest spell on record.

In South America

Parts of the Amazon River basin struck by drought reached their lowest water levels in recorded history.

(Source: http://seattletimes.nwsource.com/html/
businesstechnology/2013716921_apyescidisastrousyear.html)

4. Major Wildfire Disasters

In Australia

Eastern Australia braced for more fires and floods, as the south faced extreme heat and heavy rains threatened to swell floodwaters ravaging the north. A once-in-a-century heat wave was forecast to intensify over the weekend with high temperatures and dry winds producing the worst wildfire conditions in 25 years.

(Source: http://www.google.com/hostednews/afp/article/
ALeqM5gyUztdckUqzd_SFg9jClfRmHlWEg)

In Russia

In August 2010, Russian forest and peat fires burned out of control, continuing to rage in much of the country's European territory, with seven Russian regions declaring states of emergency. In total, 520 fires are blazing across Russia, over a total area of 188,525 hectares (465,000 acres). Close to 650,000 hectares had been burned

(Source: http://online.wsj.com/article/SB10001424052748
7040179045754088339528720388.html)

5. Major Global Flood Disasters

Flooding alone this year killed more than 6,300 people in 59 nations through September, according to the World Health Organization.

According to Swiss Re, through November 30, nearly 260,000 people died in natural disasters in 2010. Also, disasters caused $222 billion in economic losses in 2010—more than Hong Kong's economy.

(Source: http://seattletimes.nwsource.com/html/
businesstechnology/2013716921_apyescidisastrousyear.html)

In China

In 2010 large swathes of China were hit by summer rains that triggered the worst floods in a decade, caused countless deadly landslides and caused many large rivers to swell to dangerous levels. 1.4-million homes were destroyed by the flooding, which also caused 275-billion yuan (41-billion dollars) in direct economic losses.

China's northeast was the worst-hit area, with entire towns flooded and rivers bordering North Korea swollen to critical levels, prompting fears of inundations in both countries.

(Source: http://www.google.com/hostednews/afp/article/
ALeqM5juX85JVgP2tsnqUSZxNgLuXejxDw)

In Pakistan

The 2010 Pakistan floods began in July following heavy monsoon rains. Over 2,000 people have died, and over a million homes have been destroyed. And an estimated 20-million people are injured or homeless.

(Source: http://en.wikipedia.org/wiki/2010_Pakistan_floods)

In Australia

In January 2011, Queensland, Australia was hit by massive flooding described as a disaster of "biblical proportions." More than 20 towns were cut off or flooded across an area larger than France and Germany. The crisis was triggered by Australia's wettest spring on record. At least six river systems across Queensland broke their banks. The floods affected about 200,000 people, and many were evacuated. The damage could cost billions of Australian dollars to repair.

(Source: http://www.bbc.co.uk/news/world-asia-pacific-12102126)

6. Major Global Earthquake Disasters

In China

- A magnitude 8 quake in May 2008 in Sichuan province devastated a huge area of southwestern China, leaving at least 87,000 people dead or missing.
- A 6.2 magnitude quake rattled Golmud in August 2009, triggering landslides and the collapse of about 30 homes.
- In April, 2010, at least 589 people were killed and more than 10,000 injured after a magnitude 6.9 earthquake struck Western China.

(Source: http://www.telegraph.co.uk/news/worldnews/asia/
china/7588401/China-earthquake-kills-hundreds.html)

In Iceland and other countries

A volcano paralyzed air traffic for days in Europe, disrupting travel for more than seven-million people. Other volcanoes in the Congo, Guatemala, Ecuador, the Philippines and Indonesia sent people scurrying for safety. That's after flooding, landslides and more quakes killed hundreds earlier in the year.

In Indonesia

In a 24-hour period in October, Indonesia got the trifecta of terra terror: a deadly magnitude 7.7 earthquake, a tsunami that killed more than 500 people and a volcano that caused more than 390,000 people to flee.

(Source: http://seattletimes.nwsource.com/html/
businesstechnology/2013716921_apyescidisastrousyear.html)

Around the World

In early January 2010 three strong earthquakes struck the **Solomon Islands**, followed only weeks later by the 7.0 quake that leveled part of **Haiti**, leaving more than a million people homeless, killing more than 230,000 and injuring 300,000. **Korea** and Japan were also rocked. Then **Chile** was hit by an 8.8 earthquake, one of the strongest ever measured. More seismic events followed in **Japan, Mexico, Sumatra and most recently western China**. As of April (2010) the combined death toll from these natural disasters is almost 250,000. (Source: http://www.businessweek.com/news/2010-04-15/killer-quakes-on-rise-with-cities-on-fault-lines-roger-bilham.html)

7. World Food Shortage

Unpredictable weather threatens stability of food supplies:

On Tuesday, September 7, 2010, the Sri Lankan-based International Water Management Institute (IWMI) presented a report to an international gathering of scientists at World Water Week in Stockholm, Sweden. Warning that climate change is bringing more erratic rainfall, the report stated that the unreliable timing and variable amounts of rain are having increasingly noticeable effects on food security and economic growth.

This is due in part to the fact that approximately 66% of crops in Asia are fed only by rain rather than irrigated, while in Africa a full 94% are rain-fed. Highlighting these recent examples of extremely dry conditions leading to this summer's devastating Russian fires and the opposite in the calamitous Pakistani floods, Sunita Narain, head of India's Center for Science and Environment (CSE) stated, "We are getting to a point where we are getting more water, more rainy days, but it's more variable, so it leads to droughts and it leads to floods."

(Source: http://www.france24.com/en/20100907-erratic-global-weather-threatens-food-security)

8. Global Warming: Degree-by-Degree Guide

If global warming continues at the current rate, we could be facing extinction. So what exactly is going to happen as the Earth heats up? Here is a degree-by-degree guide, excepted from *Six Degrees: Our Future on a Hotter Planet*, by Mark Lynas, in *National Geographic*, January 22, 2008 (Lynus, M, 2007)

1° C Increase

Ice-free sea absorbs more heat and accelerates global warming; fresh water lost from a third of the world's surface; low-lying coastlines flooded.
Chance of avoiding one degree of global warming: zero.

2° C Increase

Europeans dying of heatstroke; forests ravaged by fire; stressed plants beginning to emit carbon rather than absorbing it; a third of all species face extinction.
Chance of avoiding two degrees of global warming: 93%, but only if emissions of greenhouse gases are reduced by 60% over the next 10 years.

3° C Increase

Carbon release from vegetation and soils speeds global warming; death of the Amazon rainforest; super-hurricanes hit coastal cities; starvation in Africa.
Chance of avoiding three degrees of global warming: poor, if the rise reaches two degrees and triggers carbon-cycle feedbacks from soils and plants.

4° C Increase

Runaway thaw of permafrost makes global warming unstoppable; much of Britain made uninhabitable by severe flooding; Mediterranean region abandoned. Chance of avoiding four degrees of global warming: poor, if the rise reaches three degrees and triggers a runaway thaw of permafrost.

5° C Increase

Methane from ocean floor accelerates global warming; ice gone from both poles; humans migrate in search of food and try vainly to live like animals off the land. Chance of avoiding five degrees of global warming: negligible, if the rise reaches four degrees and releases trapped methane from the seabed.

6° C Increase

Life on Earth ends with apocalyptic storms, flash floods, hydrogen sulphide gas and methane fireballs racing across the globe with the power of atomic bombs; only fungi survive. Chance of avoiding six degrees of global warming: zero, if the rise passes five degrees, by which time all feedbacks will be running out of control.

9. **Pollution from Livestock Waste**

In the United States

- About 13 percent of the domestic drinking-water wells in the Midwest contain unsafe levels of nitrates from fertilizers and manure lagoon spills or leaks.
- In 2001, the EPA forced five hog-factory farms to supply bottled water for local residents because activities at the farms had contaminated the local drinking water.
- A 1997 study found that 82 percent of animal-farming operations were producing nitrogen in excess of land capacity and 64 percent with excess phosphorus were poultry operations.
- A recent report by the Chesapeake Bay Foundation identified chicken manure as the primary cause of pollution in the bay.

(Source: http://www.hsus.org/farm/resources/pubs/gve/for_the_environment.html)

10. **The Noble Quality (NQ) of Animals and Humans**

"Through meditation I have discovered that the Noble Quality (NQ) of different species can be measured as a percentage to show how they embody the qualities of compassion and selflessness.

Dogs and pigs, for example, each have an impressive NQ of 30%. Cows have an NQ of 40%. In contrast, animals with more violent or flesh-eating tendencies have lower NQs. Lions, for example, have an NQ of 3% and tigers, 4%.

And as for humans, while some of us have—you know, general break down—some of us have NQs of 10%, many of us have just a 3% Noble Quality. Humans can learn from these examples of Noble Quality in our co-inhabitants." —Supreme Master Ching Hai

The Loving Quality (LQ) of Animals and Humans

"It is the unconditional, loving quality beyond the love of husband and wife, mother and son, the love we have for all beings. We are ready to sacrifice and help, be it our benefactor, stranger or enemy." —Supreme Master Ching Hai

Below are the Loving Quality (LQ) percentages of some representative animals and of humans that Master Ching Hai has shared from Her heavenly insights:

- **Domestic Animals:** Range from 80% to 300%

Dog	110%	Pig	120%
Chicken	90%	Buffalo	110%
Horse	180%		

- **Wild Animals:** Range from 20% to 300%

Wild monkey	100%	Bear	110%
Elephant	100%	Whale	300%
Cows	300%	Dolphin	110%
Tiger	20%	Lion	21%

- **Humans:** Average is 20%
  The highest on this planet: 90%
  The lowest on this planet: 5%
  Saints/sages: Thousands % and they are not human!

"NQ and LQ are both important while IQ may or may not! We should cultivate this LQ. Humans should retrospect [on] how we spend our precious time (short time) in this planet." —Supreme Master Ching Hai

NOTES

Chapter 1

1. Supreme Master TV, "Climate Change Public Service Announcements: What the VIPs Say," SupremeMasterTV.com/bbs/tb.php/sos_video/17.
2. The UN study referred to here is Henning Steinfeld et al., *Livestock's Long Shadow: Environmental Issues and Options*. The Food and Agriculture Organization of the United Nations, 2006.
3. Robert Goodland and Jeff Anhang found that "livestock contributes to 32,564 million tons of GHG annually, which equals 51percent of global GHG emissions." See their article, "Livestock and Climate Change," *World Watch Magazine*, (Nov/Dec, 2009), 10-19. http://www.worldwatch.org/node/6294.
4. Ibid, 11.
5. This is because when grain is fed to animals reared for human consumption, 90% of the energy from the original grain is lost.
6. Supreme Master TV, "Climate Change Public Service Announcements."
7. Lucas Reijnders and Sam Soret, "Quantification of the Environmental Impact of Different Dietary Protein Choices," *The American Journal of Clinical Nutrition*, Vol. 78, No. 3 (September 2003), 664S-668S. http://www.ajcn.org/content/78/3/664S.full.
8. World Food Organization, "Hunger Stats," http://www.wfp.org/hunger/stats.
9. UNEP, *Assessing the Environmental Impacts of Consumption and Production*. June, 2010. http://www.unep.fr/scp/publications/details.asp?id=DTI/1262/PA.
10. Goodland and Anhang, "Livestock and Climate Change", 15.
11. See Elke Stehfest et al., "Climate Benefits of Changing Diet." Netherlands Environmental Assessment Agency. Available online at http://www.pbl.nl/en/publications/2009/Climate-benefits-of-changing-diet.html.
12. This study by the SIWI and IWMI (Stockholm International Water Institute and International Water Management Institute), "Saving Water from Field to Fork" (May 2008) found that 70% of clean water is fed to livestock. http://www.siwi.org/documents/Resources/Policy_Briefs/PB_From_Filed_to_Fork_2008.pdf. The Center for International Forestry Research (Indonesia) states that 60-70 percent of deforestation in Brazil's Amazon rainforest results from cattle ranches. See the Center for International Forestry Research, "The Impact of the Growing Demand for Beef on the Amazon Rainforest in Brazil," April 2, 2004, http://www.mongabay.com/external/brazil_beef_amazon.htm. Also see Cees de Haan et al., *Livestock and the Environment: Finding a Balance*, Chapter 2. http://www.fao.org/ag/againfo/programmes/en/lead/toolbox/FAO/Main1/index.htm.

13. In an article published in *The Guardian*, April 15, 2008, columnist George Monbiot quotes the FAO's statistics and states, "While 100m tons of food will be diverted this year to feed cars, 760 m tonnes will be snatched from the mouths of humans to feed animals. This could cover the global food deficit 14 times. If you care about hunger, eat less meat." http://www.guardian.co.uk/commentisfree/2008/apr/15/food.biofuels?INTCMP=SRCH.

14. In February 2009 the Netherlands Environmental Assessment Agency published a new report including recommendations for Dutch and international policies on environmental sustainability. The report concludes that US$20 trillion or 50 percent of a total US$40-trillion estimated cost could be saved from a global shift to a low-meat diet. And a worldwide transition to a completely vegan diet with no animal products would save an enormous 80% by 2050. See Elke Stehfest et al., "Climate Benefits of Changing Diet," The Netherlands Environmental Assessment Agency, 2009, abstract online at http://www.pbl.nl/en/publications/2009/Climate-benefits-of-changing-diet.html. Also see Supreme Master TV's interview with Dr. Joop Oude Lohuis, head of department at the Netherlands Environmental Assessment Agency entitled "Global Shift to Vegan Diet Could Cut Climate Change Mitigation Costs by 80% : PBL study," available online at http://SupremeMasterTV.com/bbs/tb.php/sos_video/95.

15. Ibid.

Chapter 2

16. NASA climate scientist Jay Zwally describes the urgency of the situation as follows: "The Arctic Ocean could be nearly ice-free at the end of summer 2012, much faster than previous predictions." See "Arctic Ice 'could be gone in five years.'" *The Telegraph*, December 12, 2007. http://www.telegraph.co.uk/earth/earthnews/3318239/Arctic-ice-could-be-gone-in-five-years.html.

17. Scientists from the National Snow and Ice Data Center have found that in the year 2009, ice older than two years accounted for less than 10% of the ice cover at the end of February. See "Arctic Sea Ice Younger, Thinner as Melt Season Begins," in *Arctic Ice News and Analysis*, April 6, 2009, http://nsidc.org/arcticseaicenews/2009/040609.html.

18. Director of the National Snow and Ice Data Center, Dr. Mark Serreze states, "We could very well be in that quick slide downward in terms of passing a tipping point. It's tipping now. We're seeing it happen now," quoted in R. Black, "Arctic Ice 'is at tipping point," *BBC News*, August 28, 2008. http://news.bbc.co.uk/2/hi/7585645.stm . The National Snow and Ice Data Center in the US also notes, "Arctic sea ice generally reaches its annual minimum extent in mid-September. This August [2010], [the] ice extent was the second lowest in the satellite record, after 2007. On September 3 [2010], [the] ice extent dropped below the seasonal minimum for 2009 to become the third lowest in the satellite record. The Northwest Passage and the Northern Sea Route are largely free of ice, allowing the potential for a circumnavigation of the Arctic Ocean." Please see "Updated minimum Arctic sea ice extent," September 27, 2010, http://nsidc.org/arcticseaicenews/2010/092710.html.

19. Jonathan L. Bamber, "Reassessment of the Potential Sea-Level Rise from a Collapse of the West Antarctic Ice Sheet." *Science,* May 15, 2009, 324: 901-903 [DOI: 10.1126/science.1169335] (in Research Articles). Abstract online at http://www.sciencemag.org/content/324/5929/901.short.

20. From the U.S. Geological Survey, "The Water Cycle: Water Storage in Ice and Snow." Available online at http://ga.water.usgs.gov/edu/watercycleice.html.

21. The International Organization for Migration, "Migration, Climate Change, and Environmental Degradation: A Complex Nexus." Available online at http://www.iom.int/jahia/Jahia/complex-nexus.

22. At the 3rd Conference of the Parties of the UNFCCC held in Kyoto, Japan, H.E. Maumoon Abdul Gayoom (Maldives) called on world leaders to address climate change as follows: "The Maldives is one of the small states. We are not in a position to change the course of events in the world. But what you do or do not do here will greatly influence the fate of my people. It can also change the course of world history."

23. "Methane Bubbling From Arctic Lakes, Now And At End Of Last Ice Age," *Science Daily,* October 26, 2007, http://www.sciencedaily.com/releases/2007/10/071025174618.htm. Also see "Scientists Find Increased Methane Levels in Arctic Ocean," *Science Daily,* December 18, 2008, http://www.sciencedaily.com/releases/2008/12/081217203407.htm. In a number of recent reports scientists have documented the intense methane release from seabed areas near East Siberia, Russia, and Spitsbergen. See, for example, Judith Burns, "Methane Seeps from Arctic Sea-bed," *BBC News,* August 19, 2009, http://news.bbc.co.uk/2/hi/8205864.stm. Also Steve Connor, "Exclusive: The Methane Time Bomb," *The Independent,* September 23, 2009, http://www.independent.co.uk/environment/climate-change/exclusive-themethane-timebomb-938932.html.

24. See John Atcheson, "Ticking Time Bomb," *Baltimore Sun,* December 15, 2004, from http://www.commondreams.org/views04/1215-24.htm.

25. Dr. Gregory Ryskin of Northwestern University discussed his research indicating that 250-million years ago methane explosions from the ocean caused extinctions of 90% of marine species and 75% of terrestrial species, adding, "If it happened once, it could happen again." http://pangea.stanford.edu/research/Oceans/GES205/methaneGeology.pdf.

26. For example, in an interview with Supreme Master Television, Indian Glaciologist Dr. Jagdish Bahadur discussed the relationship between glacial retreat and disasters such as floods and droughts as follows: "Himalayan glaciers are in general on retreat as anywhere else on the planet due to global warming. Continued melting at the current rate will result in massive flooding. Immediately when glaciers recede they release more water, followed by severe drought." Supreme Master TV, "The Himalayan Glaciers Are Disappearing," March 25, 2009. http://suprememastertv.com/bbs/board.php?bo_table=sos_video&wr_id=83&goto_url.

27. United States Environmental Protection Agency, "Climate Change-Health and Environmental Effect: Extreme Events," http://www.epa.gov/climatechange/effects/extreme.html.

28. Anne Minard, "No More Glaciers in Glacier National Park by 2020?" *National Geographic News*, March 2, 2009, http://news.nationalgeographic.com/news/2009/03/090302-glaciers-melting.html.

29. University of Colorado at Boulder press release, "Western Water Supplies Threatened by Climate Change: Warming climate could deplete reservoir storage in the Colorado River Basin by mid-century," July 2009. http://geology.com/press-release/colorado-river-water-supply/.

30. "Loss of Andes Glaciers Threatens Water Supply," *Tehran Times*, November 28, 2007. http://www.tehrantimes.com/index_View.asp?code=158041.

31. Pew Oceans Commission, *America's Living Oceans: Charting a Course for Sea Change: a Report to the Nation*, 2003. Available online at http://www.pewtrusts.org/our_work_report_detail.aspx?id=30009.

32. Robert J. Diaz and Rutger Rosenberg, "Spreading Dead Zones and Consequences for Marine Ecosystems," *Science*, Vol. 321, No. 5891 (2008): 926-929. http://www.precaution.org/lib/marine_dead_zones_growing.080815.pdf.

33. "Big Fish Stocks Fall 90 Percent Since 1950, Study Says," *National Geographic News* May 15, 2003, http://news.nationalgeographic.com/news/2003/05/0515_030515_fishdecline.html.

34. "Oceans' Fish Could Disappear by 2050," *Discovery News*, May 17, 2010. http://news.discovery.com/earth/oceans-fish-fishing-industry.html.

35. Robert McClure, "Dead Orca is a 'Red Alert'," *Seattle Post Intelligencer*, May 7, 2002. http://www.seattlepi.com/local/69418_whale07.shtml.

36. For example the Black Saturday bushfires that burned across the Australian state of Victoria on Saturday, February 7, 2009 produced the country's highest ever loss of life from a bushfire. 173 people died as a result of the fires and 414 were injured. http://www.abc.net.au/innovation/blacksaturday/#/stories/mosaic.

37. The World Bank, *Republic of Peru Environmental Sustainability: A Key to Poverty Reduction in Peru* June 01, 2007. http://siteresources.worldbank.org/INTPERUINSPANISH/Resources/PERU_CEA_Full_Report_eng.pdf. Also see the World Bank, "Climate Change Aspects in Agriculture: Peru Country Note", January 2009, p. 3. http://siteresources.worldbank.org/INTLAC/Resources/257803-1235077152356/Country_Note_Peru.pdf.

38. "Children Die in Harsh Peru Winter," *BBC News*, July 12, 2009. http://news.bbc.co.uk/2/hi/8146995.stm.

39. US Environmental Protection Agency, "Climate Change—Health and Environmental Effects: Extreme Events." http://www.epa.gov/climatechange/effects/extreme.html.

40. "Thirty-Eight Percent of World's Surface in Danger of Desertification," *Science Daily*, February 10, 2010. http://www.sciencedaily.com/releases/2010/02/100209183133.htm.

41. "Drought causes water shortage for five-million people in China," *Earth Times*, August 23, 2009. http://www.earthtimes.org/articles/news/282501,drought-causes-watershortage-for-5-million-people-in-china.html.

42. "Australia Wildfire Death Toll Reaches 200," *CBC News*, February 17, 2009. http://www.cbc.ca/world/story/2009/02/17/australia-wildfires.html.

43. "What is Deforestation?" Lesson Plans by Lisa M. Algee, Environmental Education PhD student, the University of California at Santa Cruz. http://kids.mongabay.com/lesson_plans/lisa_algee/deforestation.html.

44. World Wildlife Foundation, "Deforestation," http://wwf.panda.org/about_our_earth/about_forests/deforestation.

45. Yacov Tsur et al., *Pricing Irrigation Water: Principles and Cases from Developing Countries*. Washington: Resource for the Future, 2004, 220.

46. "Argentina has lost nearly 70% of its forests in a century," *France 24*, October 1, 2009. http://www.france24.com/en/20090926-argentina-has-lost-nearly-70-its-forests-century-.

47. Rhett A. Butler, "98% of Orangutan Habitat Gone in the next 15 Years," Mongabay. com, June 11, 2007, http://news.mongabay.com/2007/0611-indonesia.html. Also see UNEP, *The Last Stand of the Orangutan,* available online at http://www.unep. org/grasp/docs/2007Jan-LastStand-of-Orangutan-report.pdf.

48. More will be discussed about black carbon. It is sufficient to note here that scientists from NASA's Goddard Institute of Space Studies and Columbia University Drew Shindell and Greg Faluvegi have found black carbon is the second or third greatest individual warming agent after methane and CO_2, and is responsible for 50% of Arctic melting. See Drew Shindell and Greg Faluvegi, "Climate response to regional radiative forcing during the twentieth century," *Nature Geoscience 2* (April 2009), 294-300. Abstract online at http://www.nature.com/ngeo/journal/v2/n4/abs/ngeo473.html. Similarly, Noel Keenlyside, climate researcher at the Leibniz Institute of Marine Sciences in Germany points out, "In the Arctic and Antarctic areas, black carbon deposition on snow and ice causes the surfaces to absorb more of the sun's heat." Noel Keenlyside, "Atmospheric science: Clean air policy and Arctic warming," *Nature Geoscience* 2, (2009): 243-244. Abstract online at http:// www.nature.com/ngeo/journal/v2/n4/full/ngeo486.html.

49. Julia Whitty, "Animal Extinction: A Great Threat to Mankind," *The Independent,* April 30, 2007. http://www.independent.co.uk/environment/animal-extinction--the-greatest-threat-to-mankind-397939.html.

50. IPCC (Intergovernmental Panel of Climate Change), *Fourth Assessment Report: Changes in Atmospheric Constituents and in Radiative Forcing, 2007,* 212. Available online at http://www.ipcc.ch/pdf/assessment-report/ar4/wg1/ar4-wg1-chapter2.pdf.

51. For more details, please see the Global Humanitarian Forum study, "Climate Change The Human Impact Report: The Anatomy of a Silent Crisis." Available at http://www.eird.org/publicaciones/humanimpactreport.pdf.

52. Kevin Watkins et al., *Human Development Report 2006: Beyond scarcity: Power, poverty and the global water crisis*, United Nations Development Programme, 2006, 20, 23. http://hdr.undp.org/en/reports/global/hdr2006.

53. FAO, "1.02 Billion People Hungry—One Sixth of Humanity Undernourished—More Than Ever Before," *FAO Media Center*, June 19, 2009. http://www.fao.org/news/story/0/item/20568/icode/en.

54. Megan Rowling, "Climate Change Causes 315,000 Deaths a Year-Report," *Reuters*, May 29, 2009, http://www.reuters.com/article/idUSLS1002309.

55. Ibid.

56. "Peru Health Ministry Warns of possible dengue fever in Lima, insists on prevention," *Andean Air Mail and Peruvian Times*, March 2, 2009, http://www.peruviantimes.com/peru-health-ministry-warns-of-possible-dengue-fever-in-lima-insists-onprevention/021936.

57. It is widely accepted that global warming-induced increases in floods and droughts are fuelling the spread of epidemics in areas unprepared for the diseases. For example, a *Washington Post* report states, "Malaria is climbing the mountains to reach populations in higher elevations in Africa and Latin America. Cholera is growing in warmer seas. Dengue fever and Lyme disease are moving north. West Nile virus, never seen on this continent until seven years ago, has infected more than 21,000 people in the United States and Canada and killed more than 800. The World Health Organization has identified more than 30 new or resurgent diseases in the last three decades, the sort of explosion some experts say has not happened since the Industrial Revolution brought masses of people together in cities." See Struck, Doug, "Climate Change Drives Disease to New Territory," *The Washington Post*, May 5, 2006, http://www.washingtonpost.com/wp-dyn/content/article/2006/05/04/AR2006050401931.html. Also see Alyshah Hasham, "Climate change spreads infectious diseases worldwide," *International News Services,* http://www.internationalnewsservices.com/articles/1-latest-news/17833-climate-change-spreads-infectious-diseases-worldwide.

58. From "Scientists: 'Arctic is Screaming': Global Warming May Have Passed Tipping Point," *Fox News*, December 12, 2007. Available online at http://www.foxnews.com/ story/0,2933,316501,00.html.

59. From FAO, "Livestock a major threat to environment: Remedies urgently needed." *FAO Newsroom*, November 29, 2006. Available online at http://www.fao.org/newsroom/en/news/2006/1000448/index.html.

60. From Peter Fricker, "Care about the environment? Eat less meat," *Global and Mail*, Jan. 23, 2008. Available online at http://www.theglobeandmail.com/news/world/article661961.ece.

61. Jerry Mayer and John P. Holms eds, *Bite-size Einstein: Quotations on Just About Everything from the Greatest Mind of the Twentieth Century.* St. Martin's Press, New York, 1996, p. 10.

Chapter 3

62. IPCC, *Fourth Assessment Report*, 212.

63. Kirk Smith, "Methane Controls Before Risky Geo-engineering, Please," *New Scientist* 2714 (June 25, 2009). http://www.goodplanet.info/eng/Contenu/Points-de-vues/Methane-controls-before-risky-geoengineering-please/(theme)/268.

64. Goodland and Anhang, "Livestock and Climate Change."

65. William Collins, Professor of Earth and Planetary Science, the University of California, Berkeley, U.S.A. has already pointed out the abrupt changes in climate that methane can induce: "Methane gas molecules locked inside cages of water ice are in such a concentrated form that when the ice melts they expand to 164 times their frozen volume and are 72 times more potent than carbon dioxide as a GHG." See Peter Preuss, "Impacts: On the Threshold of Abrupt Climate Change." *Berkeley Lab News Letter*, September 17, 2008, http://newscenter.lbl.gov/feature-stories/2008/09/17/impactson-the-threshold-of-abrupt-climate-changes/.

66. For more details on methane release from the sea, see Cornelia Dean, "Study Says Undersea Release of Methane Is Under Way," *The New York Times*, March 04, 2010, http://www.nytimes.com/2010/03/05/science/earth/05methane.html. Also see Michael

Fitzpatric, "Methane release 'looks stronger," *BBC News*, Jan.6, 2010, http://news.bbc.co.uk/2/hi/8437703.stm. For methane release from lakes, see Katey M. Walter et al., "Methane production and bubble emissions from arctic lakes: Isotopic implications for source pathways and ages," *Journal of Geophysical Research* 113, http://www.fs.fed.us/pnw/pubs/journals/pnw_2008_Walter001.pdf. Also see Katey M. Walter et al., "Methane bubbling from Siberian thaw lakes as a positive feedback to climate warming," *Nature* (2006) 443. http://www.nature.com/nature/journal/v443/n7107/abs/nature05040.html.

67. Katey Walter, "Siberian Lakes Burp 'Time-Bomb' Greenhouse Gas," *Science Daily*, September 8, 2006. http://www.sciencedaily.com/releases/2006/09/060908094051.htm.

68. Peter Ward, "Impact From the Deep," *Scientific American*, September 18, 2006, http://www.scientificamerican.com/article.cfm?id=impact-from-the-deep&sc=I100322 , and Supreme Master TV, "Learning from the Past: Mass Extinctions and Global Warming with Dr. Peter Ward," Sept. 23, 2009, http://suprememastertv.com/pe/?wr_id=87&page=4&page=4#v. Also L.R. Kump, A. Pavlov and M. A. Arthur, "Massive release of hydrogen sulfide to the surface ocean and atmosphere during intervals of oceanic anoxia," *Geology*, v. 33 (2005), 397-400.

69. Scientists have found that "the livestock industry [including meat, eggs and dairy] are responsible for 65% of worldwide, human-caused nitrous oxide emissions." See Steinfeld et al., *Livestock's Long Shadow*, 114.

70. A number of studies have addressed this issue, particularly those by Professor Heitor Evangelista and colleagues of Janeiro State University in Brazil, Professor Mark Jackson of the University of California at Berkeley, Greenpeace and Friends of the Earth. See news reports by Lauren Morello, "Cutting Soot Emissions May Slow Climate Change in the Arctic," *Scientific American*, August 2, 2010, http://www.scientificamerican.com/article.cfm?id=cutting-soot-emissions-may-slow-climate-change-in-the-arctic as well as by Randy Boswell, "Soot Is Second Leading Cause of Climate Change: Study," *Ottawa Citizen*, August 1, 2010, http://www.ottawacitizen.com/technology/Soot+second+leading+cause+climate+change+study/3349011/story.html?cid=megadrop_story#ixzz0vekfEf8s.

71. See "An Interview with Dr. Kirk Smith, Professor of Global Environmental Health at UC Berkeley," Supreme Master TV, July 1, 2008, SupremeMasterTV.com/bbs/tb.php/sos_video/21.

72. Monica Bruckner, "The Gulf of Mexico Dead Zone," http://serc.carleton.edu/microbelife/topics/deadzone.

73. SIWI and IWMI, "Saving Water from Field to Fork." Also see Natural Resources Defense Council, "Facts about Pollution from Livestock Farms," http://www.nrdc.org/water/pollution/ffarms.asp.

74. Robert J. Diaz and Rutger Rosenberg, "Spreading Dead Zones and Consequences for Marine Ecosystems."

75. Dr. Andrew Bakun and his colleague, Dr. Scarla Weeks of the University of Cape Town in South Africa, have found that overfishing of sardines off the southwest coast of Africa may have been a factor in eruptions of two toxic gases—hydrogen sulfide, and methane— from the Atlantic Ocean floor. Hydrogen sulfide causes

a horrible, rotten-egg smell that had long burdened (and perplexed) residents of local communities in Namibia, while also poisoning fish and causing oxygen poor dead zones in the water. See Andrew Bakun and Scarla J. Weeks, "Greenhouse gas buildup, sardines, submarine eruptions and the possibility of abrupt degradation of intense marine upwelling ecosystems" *Ecology Letters* (2004) vol.7, issue 11, 1015–1023. http://woldlab.caltech.edu/~tristan/silence/bakun_2004_eco_letters.pdf.

76. From Thomas Lane, "UN Official Warns on Fisheries Losses." *BBC News*, May 21, 2010. http://www.bbc.co.uk/news/10128900.

77. David Pimentel, ecologist and Professor Emeritus at Cornell University, USA warns, "With 87% of total water used for livestock production, the United States will soon become a water-stressed country." Pimentel, "U.S. could feed 800-million people with grain that livestock eat, Cornell ecologist advises animal scientists," *Cornell Science News*, August 7, 1997. http://www.news.cornell.edu/releases/aug97/livestock.hrs.html.

78. See, for example, Anne Minard, "No More Glaciers in Glacier National Park by 2020?" *National Geographic News*, March 2, 2009, http://news.nationalgeographic.com/news/2009/03/090302-glaciers-melting.html. For a scholarly report, see R. D. Moore et al., "Glacier change in western North America: influences on hydrology, geomorphic hazards and water quality," *Hydrological Processes* 23 (2009), 42–61. DOI: 10.1002/hyp.7162. http://www.glaciers.pdx.edu/fountain/MyPapers/MooreEtAl2009_GlacierChangeWaterRunoff.pdf.

79. A classic study on this topic is Marcia Kreith, *Water Inputs in California Food Production*, prepared for the Water Education Foundation, Sacramento, CA. 1991. http://www.sakia.org/cms/fileadmin/content/irrig/general/kreith_1991_water_inputs_in_ca_food_production-excerpt.pdf.

80. Marlow Vesterby and Kenneth S. Krupa, *Major Uses of Land in the United States, 1997* (SB973) September 2001, http://www.ers.usda.gov/publications/sb973/sb973.pdf.

81. See The United Nations Convention to Combat Desertification (UNCCD), "Ten Years on: UN marks World Day to Combat Desertification," June 17, 2004, http://www.unccd.int/publicinfo/pressrel/showpressrel.php?pr=press01_06_04.

82. Yacov Tsur et al., *Pricing Irrigation Water: Principles and Cases from Developing Countries*, 220.

83. Juliet Gellatley and Tony Hardle, *The Silent Ark: A Chilling Exposé of Meat.* HarperCollins Publishers Ltd., 1996.

84. Harvey Blatt, *America's Food: What You don't Know about What You Eat.* Boston: MIT Press, 2008, 136.

85. From "The Science and Solution to Global Warming," Supreme Master Television, August 2008. SupremeMasterTV.com/bbs/tb.php/sos_video/16.

86. According to IPCC scientists, deforestation or forest clearing contributes from 17.4% to up to one third of world atmospheric GHG emissions. See IPCC, *Fourth Assessment Report, Synthetic Report*, Section 2, p. 36 and *Working Group Report*, section 7, p. 527.

87. John Robbins, *Diet for a New America*, excerpted from http://whitt.ca/soapbox/vegetarian.html.

88.   Julie Denslow and Christine Padoch, *People of the Tropical Rainforest*. Berkeley: University of California Press, 1988, 169.

89.   See Greenpeace UK, "The Congo Rainforest of Central Africa," http://www. greenpeace.org.uk/forests/congo.

90.   A study by the Rodale Institute, USA states, "Even though climate and soil type affect [CO_2] sequestration capacities, these multiple research efforts verify that practical organic agriculture if practiced on the planet's 3.5-billion tillable acres, could sequester nearly 40 % of current CO_2 emissions." See Timothy LaSalle and Paul Hepperly, "Regenerative Organic Farming: A Solution to Global Warming," 2008.   Available online at http://www.rodaleinstitute.org/files/Rodale_Research_Paper-07_30_08.pdf.

91.   In an interview with Supreme Master Television, Professor of Geophysical Sciences at the University of Chicago Dr. David Archer states, "It's very clear that when you grow grain and then feed it to animals and then eat the animals, you lose 90% of the energy from the original grain, and so not only can you feed fewer people on the agriculture that you have but as they discovered, it also requires a lot more fossil fuel energy to make that happen." See Supreme Master TV, "The Science and Solution to Climate Change," http://suprememastertv.com/bbs/board.php?bo_table=sos_video&wr_id=16.   Also, Earth Save International has summarized the high cost of meat production as follows: "12 pounds of grain: Makes eight loaves of bread or two plates of spaghetti. 55 square feet of rainforest: For every pound of rainforest beef, approximately 600 pounds of precious, living matter is destroyed, including 20 to 30 plant species, over 100 insect species and dozens of mammals and reptiles. 2,500 gallons of water: This could be used to grow more than 50 pounds of fruits and vegetables." See Earth Save International, "The Hamburger Poster," http://www.earthsave.org/support/hamburgerSMALL.pdf.

92.   John Robbins, *Diet for a New America: How Your Food Choices Affect Your Health, Happiness and the Future of Life on Earth*. Tiburon: H. J. Kramer, 1987, 367.

93.   Here are some numbers and statistics: According to a study by the International Union for the Conservation of Nature, 30% of the world's mammal, bird and amphibian species are currently threatened with extinction due to human actions. See The Millennium Ecosystem Assessment Report, 2005, http://maweb.org/en/Reports.aspx. Over a million species will be lost in the coming 50 years. Moreover, among 45,000 species monitored by IUCN, 40% were threatened with extinction in 2008. See "IUCN Red List reveals world's mammals in crisis," IUCN News release, October 6, 2008. http://www.iucn.org/search.cfm?uNewsID=1695.

94.   The US General Accounting Office long ago established that overall livestock produce 130 times more waste than humans. Pigs produce three times the excrement that humans do, and cows produce 21 times the amount of waste generated by humans. See *Animal Agriculture Waste Management Practice*, 1999, http://www.gao.gov/archive/1999/rc99205.pdf.

95.   F. Ackerman and E. A. Stanton, Climate Change—the Costs of Inaction: Report to Friends of the Earth England, Wales and Northern Ireland, 2006. http://www.foe.co.uk/resource/reports/econ_costs_cc.pdf.   Also see F. Ackerman, *Climate Change: The Costs of Inaction: Testimony presented to: United States Congress House*

Committee on Energy and Commerce, 2009. http://www.e3network.org/opeds/Ackerman_testimony_April22.pdf.

96. From B. Barrett and A., Lim, "Japan to suffer huge climate costs." *OurWorld 2.0* (United Nations University), June 30, 2009. http://ourworld.unu.edu/en/japan-examines-costs-of-climate-change/.

97. Elke Stehfest et al., "Climate Benefits of Changing Diet," The Netherlands Environmental Assessment Agency, 2009. Available online at http://www.pbl.nl/en/publications/2009/Climate-benefits-of-changing-diet.html.

98. See "Heart Disease and Stroke Statistics 2010 Update: A Report From the American Heart Association," *Circulation*, 2010; 121; e46-e215 p. e206. http://circ.ahajournals.org/cgi/content/full/121/7/e46.

99. See the Centers for Disease Control and Prevention study, "Diabetes: Success and Opportunities for Population-Based Prevention and Control: At a Glance 2010" http://www.cdc.gov/chronicdisease/resources/publications/aag/ddt.htm. Also, F. G. Jansman et al., "Cost considerations in the treatment of colorectal cancer", *Pharmacoeconomics*. No. 25 (2007), 537-562. Abstract online at http://ideas.repec.org/a/wkh/phecon/v25y2007i7p537-562.html.

100. These passages are taken from Supreme Master Ching Hai's interview with journalist Ben Murnane on July 7, 2009. The interview was published in the July 12, 2009 issue of the *Irish Sunday Independent*, Ireland, under the title, "An Urgent Call to Save Our Planet." See the interview in video: http://www.suprememastertv.com/wow/?wr_id=365&page=9&page=9#v.

101. Foodwatch, *Organic: A Climate Saviour? The Foodwatch report on the greenhouse effect of conventional and organic farming in Germany.* May 2009. http://foodwatch.de/foodwatch/content/e6380/e24459/e24474/foodwatch_report_on_the_greenhouse_effect_of_farming_05_2009_ger.pdf.

102. Ibid.

103. See Gowri Koneswaran and Danielle Nierenberg, "Global Farm Animal Production and Global Warming: Impacting and Mitigating Climate Change" (discussion section), *Environmental Health Perspectives*, 116(5) (May 2008): 578-582, http://www.ncbi.nlm.nih.gov/pmc/articles/PMC2367646.

104. William Lambers, "25,000 die of hunger each day," *History News Network* (George Mason University), October 7, 2007, http://hnn.us/articles/27396.html.

Chapter 4

105. At a video conference held in January 2008 in Los Angeles, USA, Supreme Master Ching Hai responded to a question about what message she would give to world leaders. This paragraph is part of her answer.

106. In September 2010, the number of countries that had enacted smoking bans reached 94.

107. World Watch Institute, "Matters of Scale -The Price of Beef," *World Watch Magazine*, Jul/Aug 1994. Available online at http://www.worldwatch.org/node/791.

108. In recent years, farm subsidies have remained high in the United States even in years of near-record profits. The US government pays about $20-25 billion direct

subsidies to farmers annually. According to the USDA 2006 Fiscal Year Budget, animal-feedgrain subsidies alone comprised more than 35% of this total. Between 2003 and 2004, the US spent $3.6 billion on animal-feed corn and soy each year. This made the feed grain available below cost. See the Institute of Agriculture and Trade Policy, Trade and Global Governance Program, "Below-Cost Feed Crops: An Indirect Subsidy for Industrial Animal Factories," June 2006, http://www.worc.org/userfiles/IATP%20cheap%20grain.pdf.

109. *Slaughterhouse: The Shocking Story of Greed, Neglect and Inhumane Treatment Inside the U.S. Meat Industry*, by Gail A. Eisnitz (Human Farming Association, 2006) shows that one hamburger can contain *up to 100 different cows, and that one infected cow can contaminate up to 16 tons of beef.*

110. AlterNet.org Editors, "The Seven Deadly Myths of Industrial Agriculture: Myth Three," September 5, 2002, http://www.alternet.org/story/13904.

111. By 2008, eleven organic gardens were already operating in the township; for example, see Helen Kilbey, "South Africa: Cape Town Goes Organic," *AllAfrica. com*, January 14, 2008, http://www.regoverningmarkets.org/en/news/southern_africa/south_africa_cape_town_goes_organic.html. Also see "From the Ground Up: Organic Gardening Fuels a Food Revolution," *AllAfrica.com*, January 9, 2008, http://allafrica.com/specials/organic_food_sa.

112. A new fertilizer imported from Tanzania has helped Kenyan farmers reduce soil acidity and increase per-hectare yields of cereal grains such as maize by 30 per cent. In Uganda, agricultural productivity is expected to increase following a recent pledge by Korea to construct an organic fertilizer factory there. See Ministry of Agriculture, Republic of Kenya, "Farmers to Reap Maximum Benefits from Organic Fertilizer," http://www.kilimo.go.ke/index.php?option=com_content&view=artic le&catid=149%3Anews&id=266%3Afarmers-to-reap-maximum-benefits-from-organicfertilizer&Itemid=46.

113. "Organic food has long been considered a niche market and a luxury for wealthy consumers. Researchers in Denmark found, however, that there would not be any serious negative effect on food security for sub-Saharan Africa if 50% of agricultural land in the food exporting regions of Europe and North America were converted to organic by 2020." See "Researchers: Organic push won't hurt world food supply," *USA Today*, May 5, 2007, ftp://ftp.fao.org/paia/organicag/OFS/press4.pdf.

114. According to the IFOAM, the current global market for organic foods and drinks is estimated to be around US$50 billion, and increased by 10-20 per cent annually from 2000 to 2007. This sub-sector provides a unique export opportunity for many developing countries because 97 percent of its revenues are generated in the OECD countries, while 80 percent of its producers are found in the developing countries of Africa, Asia and Latin America. See UNEP, "Organic Agriculture in Uganda," http://www.unep.org/greeneconomy/SuccessStories/OrganicAgricultureinUganda/tabid/4655/language/en-US/Default.aspx. Also see UNEP, "Environment-Led Green Revolution Key to Future Food Security in Africa," Press Release, May 14, 2009, http://www.grida.no/news/press/3680.aspx.

115. Ivette Perfecto et al., "Organic Agriculture and the Global Food Supply," *Renewable Agriculture and Food Systems*, 22 (2007): 86-108. http://agr.wa.gov/Foodanimal/Organic/Certificate/2008/NewsRelease/BadgleyResearchPaper.pdf.

116. "Organic farms 'best for wildlife,'" *BBC News*, August 3, 2005. http://news.bbc. co.uk/2/hi/uk_news/4740609.stm.

117. See Al Meyerhoff, "The loss of billions of bees raises questions about our pesticide controls," *Los Angeles Times*, July 30, 2008, http://beediary.wordpress.com/tag/ccd.

118. Timothy LaSalle, "Organic farming could stop global climate change," *The Tree Hugger*, October 10, 2010. http://www.treehugger.com/files/2009/10/organic-farming-could-stop-global-climate-change.php.

119. C. Benbrook, "Simplifying the Pesticide Risk Equation: The Organic Option," *State of Science Review of the Organic Center*, March 8, 2008. http://www.organic-center. org/reportfiles/Organic_Option_Final_Ex_Summary.pdf.

120. FAO, *Organic Agriculture and Food Security* (2007). ftp://ftp.fao.org/paia/organicag/ ofs/OFS-2007-5.pdf.

121. See note 14. This refers to research by the Netherland Environmental Assessment Agency to provide recommendations for the Netherlands government and international policy making.

122. See study by the UN agency The International Fund for Agricultural Development (IFAD), "The Adoption of Organic Agriculture Among Small Farmers in Latin America and the Caribbean," April 2003, Report No. 1337. http://www.ifad.org/ evaluation/public_html/eksyst/doc/thematic/pl/organic.htm.

123. See note 14, 119.

124. See John Robbins, "The Pig Farmer," April 2010, available online at http://www. johnrobbins.info/blog/the-pig-farmer. Also see John Robbins, *The Food Revolution: How Your Diet Can Help Save Your Life and Our World*.

125. See the European Parliament, "2050, The Future begins today—Recommendations for the EU's future integrated policy on climate change," April 2, 2009. http://www. europarl.europa.eu/oeil/file.jsp?id=5626312.

126. See Jens Holms, "The EU Parliament calls meat a Climate Threat," February 4, 2009. http://jensholm.se/2009/02/04/the-eu-parliament-calls-meat-a-climate-threat.

127. See Chris Mason, "Belgian city plans 'veggie' days," *BBC News*, May 12, 2009. http://news.bbc.co.uk/2/hi/europe/8046970.stm.

128. See Candra Malik, "Prince Charles Gives $2.8b to Preserve Rain Forests," July 30, 2009. http://www.thejakartaglobe.com/news/prince-charles-gives-28b-to-preserve-rain-forests/321249.

129. See "Who's Up for a Low Carb Diet?" *Sustainable Development Commission* (Northern Ireland), June 18, 2009. http://www.sd-commission.org.uk/news. php/246/ireland/whos-up-for-a-low-carb-diet.

130. Ibid.

131. This refers to the booklet produced by Countryside Management Branch DARD entitled *Code of Good Agricultural Practice*, August 2008, which provides good management practices to avoid polluting water, air and soil. http://www.dardni.gov. uk/code_of_good_agricultural_practice_cogap_august_2008.pdf.

132. See Hawaii State Legislature, "Requesting the Board of Education to Develop a Policy to Include Vegetarian and Vegan Meal Options in All School Menu Plans," Report HCR59 HD1, offered on November 2, 2009. http://www.capitol.hawaii.gov/ session2009/Bills/HCR59_HD1_.HTM.

133. See City of Cincinnati, *Climate Protection Action Plan-the Green Cincinnati Plan*, July 19, 2008, 35, 209-211. Available online at http://www.cincinnati-oh.gov/cmgr/downloads/cmgr_pdf18280.pdf.

134. Jennifer Duck, "Bringing Home the Bacon, Vegan Style," *ABC News*, May 4, 2007, http://abcnews.go.com/Politics/story?id=3139687&page=1. Also see "Dennis Kucinich Celebrates Vegan Earth Day With A Special VEGGIE Message," http://vegdaily.com/2009/07/dennis-kucinich-celebrates-vegan-earth-day-with-a-special-veggie-message/.

135 Jason Tomassini, "Senator goes vegetarian for week," *Gazette.Net*, April 29, 2009, http://www.gazette.net/stories/04292009/takonew183650_32520.shtml. Also see Kailey Harless, "Raskin's Revolution," *VegNews.com*, May 4, 2007, www.vegnews.com/web/articles/page.do?pageId=688&catId=1.

136. Meatless Monday, "Baltimore Schools Go Meatless," http://www.meatlessmonday.com/baltimore-schools.

137. The San Francisco Vegetarian Society, "San Francisco is First U.S. City to Declare Mondays as 'Veg Day,'" April 7, 2010, http://www.vegsource.com/news/2010/04/san-francisco-is-first-us-city-to-declare-mondays-as-veg-day.html.

138. See Taiwan Environmental Information Center, "Million people sign up to resist Global Warming by adopting vegetarian diet" (in Chinese), http://e-info.org.tw/node/33565.

Chapter 5

139. In the National Survey on Giving, Volunteering and Participating (NSGVP), Statistics Canada interviewed 2,389 Canadians aged 15 to 24. See Susan Pedwell, "I want to make a difference," *Canadian Living*, http://www.canadianliving.com/life/community/i_want_to_make_a_difference.php.

140. According to World Watch research, the livestock industry contributes 51% of the greenhouse gases produced on Earth. See note 3.

141. See notes 90, p.1

142. See the Iowa Pork Producers Association, "USDA to buy more pork," November 11, 2009, http://www.iowapork.org/Newsroom/NewsForProducers/USDAporkbuy/tabid/1504/Default.aspx. Also see the National Pork Producers Council (NPPC)'s *Capital Pork Report* (November 2009), http://nppc.org/uploadedfiles/cprNOV-6.pdf.

143. Ibid.

144. More suggestions for green activities are available on the Supreme Master Television website.

145. See, for example, the Supreme Master TV documentaries, "No Water Required! Dry Farming in Âu Lac (Vietnam)," free online at http://www.suprememastertv.com/bbs/tb.php/pe/79, "Growing Fruits and Vegetables in Sand-One Story From Âu Lac (Vietnam)," SupremeMasterTV.com/bbs/tb.php/pe/72.

146. The link is SupremeMasterTV.com/sos-flyer.

147. Founded on March 7, 2008, Loving Hut vegan restaurants numbered 221 worldwide by the end of January, 2011.

BIBLIOGRAPHY OF TALKS BY
SUPREME MASTER CHING HAI

This book consists of unabridged excerpts from Supreme Master Ching Hai's talks on various occasions. The following is a complete list.

1. *The Way to Gain the Kingdom of God is through Enlightenment*, public lecture in Massachusetts, USA on February 24, 1991. SupremeMasterTV.com/bbs/tb.php/wow/451.
2. *Greening the Planet*, public lecture in California, USA on May 19, 1991. SupremeMasterTV.com/bbs/tb.php/bmd/346.
3. *Eating Meat Destroys Lives and Harms the Planet* (Part 1), international gathering in Hawaii, USA on September 3, 1994. SupremeMasterTV.com/bbs/tb.php/bmd/554.
4. *Live a Life of Conscience and Love* (Part 3), international gathering in Cambodia on May 11, 1996. SupremeMasterTV.com/bbs/tb.php/bmd/630.
5. *In Balance with Our Planetary Ecosystem*, international gathering in Florida, USA on June 6, 2001. SupremeMasterTV.com/bbs/tb.php/bmd/362.
6. *Preserving Our Beautiful Planet* (Part 2), international gathering in London, United Kingdom on October 24, 2006. SupremeMasterTV.com/bbs/tb.php/bmd/336.
7. *Simple Living to Save the Planet* (Part 1), international gathering in Austria on May 27, 2007. SupremeMasterTV.com/bbs/tb.php/bmd/336.
8. *Animals Contribute to the Health of Our Planet* (Part 2), international gathering in Paris, France on August 1, 2007. SupremeMasterTV.com/bbs/tb.php/bmd/611.
9. *Supreme Master Ching Hai on Climate Change*, international gathering in Paris, France on December 25, 2007. SupremeMasterTV.com/bbs/tb.php/bmd/307.
10. *Time to Act on Global Warming*, international gathering in Paris, France on December 26, 2007. SupremeMasterTV.com/bbs/tb.php/bmd/350.
11. *A Global Effort to Save the Planet*, teleconference with Supreme Master TV staff in Los Angeles, USA on January 20, 2008. SupremeMasterTV.com/bbs/tb.php/bmd/357.
12. *The Solution*, international gathering in Austria on February 28, 2008. SupremeMasterTV.com/bbs/tb.php/bmd/327.

13. *Go Veg, Be Green, Save the Planet*, international gathering in Monaco on May 4, 2008. SupremeMasterTV.com/bbs/tb.php/bmd/383.

14. *SOS! International Seminar on Global Warming: Saving Lives and Protecting the Earth*, international conference in Seoul, South Korea on May 22, 2008. SupremeMasterTV.com/bbs/tb.php/wow/245.

15. *Eden on Earth through Vegetarianism*, videoconference with Association members in Surrey, United Kingdom on June 12, 2008. SupremeMasterTV.com/bbs/tb.php/bmd/386.

16. *Vegetarianism is the Solution to Save the World*, videoconference with Association members in London, United Kingdom on June 13, 2008. SupremeMasterTV.com/bbs/tb.php/bmd/396.

17. *2008 Critical Moments to Save the Earth: What Can I Do?*, international conference in Taipei, Formosa (Taiwan) on June 29, 2008. SupremeMasterTV.com/bbs/tb.php/wow/254.

18. *Eden on Earth*, international arts gallery exhibition in Taipei, Formosa on July 5, 2008.

19. *Spreading the Vegetarian Solution*, videoconference with Association members in Seattle, USA on July 6, 2008. SupremeMasterTV.com/bbs/tb.php/bmd/412.

20. *Have a Positive Vision and Attitude*, videoconference with Association members in San Jose, USA on July 10, 2008. SupremeMasterTV.com/bbs/tb.php/bmd/421.

21. *Go Veg, Be Green, Do Good*, videoconference with Association members in New York, USA on July 13, 2008. SupremeMasterTV.com/bbs/tb.php/bmd/430.

22. *A Noble Goal and Change of Heart Can Save the Planet*, videoconference with Association members in Au Lac (Vietnam) on July 20, 2008. SupremeMasterTV.com/bbs/tb.php/bmd/447.

23. *Humans are Inherently Compassionate and Loving*, videoconference with Association members in Bangkok, Thailand on July 24, 2008. SupremeMasterTV.com/bbs/tb.php/bmd/455.

24. *Climate Change*, international conference in West Hollywood, USA on July 26, 2008. SupremeMasterTV.com/bbs/tb.php/wow/262.

25. *SOS: Stop Global Warming*, international conference in Tokyo, Japan on July 27, 2008. SupremeMasterTV.com/bbs/tb.php/wow/265.

26. *Leading a Virtuous Lifestyle in Accord with the Law of Love*, videoconference with Association members in Los Angles, USA on July 31, 2008. SupremeMasterTV.com/bbs/tb.php/bmd/458.

27. *Live Our Lives with Conscience and Love*, videoconference with Association members in Penghu, Formosa (Taiwan) on August 2, 2008. SupremeMasterTV.com/bbs/tb.php/bmd/467.

28. *Compassion Begets Compassion*, videoconference with Association members in Sydney, Australia on August 17, 2008. SupremeMasterTV.com/bbs/tb.php/bmd/484.

29. *Going in the Noble Direction*, videoconference with Association members in Auckland, New Zealand on August 19, 2008. SupremeMasterTV.com/bbs/tb.php/bmd/492.

30. *Find Safety & Protection by Walking the Way of Heaven*, international gathering in France on August 20, 2008. SupremeMasterTV.com/bbs/tb.php/bmd/532.

31. *Eating Meat Destroys Lives and Harms the Planet* (Part 7), international gathering in France on August 23, 2008. SupremeMasterTV.com/bbs/tb.php/bmd/554.

32. *The Only Refuge is in the Virtuous Way of Living*, videoconference with Association members in Vancouver, Canada on August 24, 2008. SupremeMasterTV.com/bbs/tb.php/bmd/514.

33. Live Interview with Supreme Master Ching Hai by East Coast FM Radio, Ireland on August 31, 2008. SupremeMasterTV.com/bbs/tb.php/wow/275.

34. Interview with Supreme Master Ching Hai by Bob Lebensold of Environmentally Sound Radio, USA on September 11, 2008. SupremeMasterTV.com/bbs/tb.php/wow/460.

35. *Stop Global Warming: Act Now*, international conference in Pathum Thani, Thailand on October 11, 2008. SupremeMasterTV.com/bbs/tb.php/wow/284.

36. *The Birds in My Life* Aulacese (Vietnamese) edition, international book premiere in Pathum Thani, Thailand on October 11, 2008. SupremeMasterTV.com/bbs/tb.php/wow/288.

37. *A Great Mission: Saving the Planet*, videoconference with Association members in California, USA on November 26, 2008. SupremeMasterTV.com/bbs/tb.php/bmd/502.

38. Interview with Supreme Master Ching Hai by East Coast Radio FM, Ireland on November 30, 2008. SupremeMasterTV.com/bbs/tb.php/wow/310.

39. *Celestial Art,* English edition international book premiere in Los Angles, USA on December 12, 2008. SupremeMasterTV.com/bbs/tb.php/wow/304.

40. *Trust in God* (Part 3), international gathering on December 16, 2008. SupremeMasterTV.com/bbs/tb.php/download/7478.

41. *Compassion is Inherent in All of Us*, international gathering on January 26, 2009.

42. *SOS International Conference* in Ulan Bator, Mongolia on January 27, 2009. SupremeMasterTV.com/bbs/tb.php/wow/314.

43. *Act Now!-For a More Peaceful and Safer World* videoconference with Supreme Master Ching Hai and Former Philippine President Fidel Ramos in Taipei, Formosa (Taiwan) on February 21, 2009. SupremeMasterTV.com/bbs/tb.php/wow/319.

44. *SOS-Save the Planet*, international conference in Xalapa, Veracruz, Mexico on March 6, 2009. SupremeMasterTV.com/bbs/tb.php/wow/326.

45. *Juice Fast for Peace* videoconference in Culver City, California, USA on March 7, 2009. SupremeMasterTV.com/bbs/tb.php/wow/331.

46. *Spiritual Practice and Sincerity Helps the Planet*, international gathering on March 8, 2009.

47. *Save Our Earth Conference 2009: Protecting the Environment and Respecting All Lives*, international conference in Seoul, South Korea on April 26, 2009. SupremeMasterTV.com/bbs/tb.php/wow/339.

48. *Be Organic Vegan to Save the Planet*, international conference in Lome, Togo on May 9, 2009. SupremeMasterTV.com/bbs/tb.php/wow/343.

49. *Let's Make the Change-Protect the Environment*, international conference in Boca del Río, Veracruz, Mexico on June 4, 2009. SupremeMasterTV.com/bbs/tb.php/wow/348.

50. *Vegan Earth Day for a Vegan World*, international conference in Woodland Hills, California, USA on June 21, 2009. SupremeMasterTV.com/bbs/tb.php/wow/355.

51. Interview with Supreme Master Ching Hai by journalist Ben Murnane on July 12, 2009, Published in the Irish Sunday Independent. SupremeMasterTV.com/bbs/tb.php/wow/365.

52. *There is an Alternative Way of Living*, international gathering on July 26, 2009.

53. Interview with Supreme Master Ching Hai by journalist Charles Norton for The House Magazine, UK on August 8, 2009. SupremeMasterTV.com/bbs/tb.php/wow/375.

54. *We Have to Save the Planet at All Cost*, international gathering on August 8, 2009. SupremeMasterTV.com/bbs/tb.php/bmd/625.

55. *Solutions for a Beautiful Planet*, international conference in Nonthaburi, Thailand on August 15, 2009. SupremeMasterTV.com/bbs/tb.php/wow/372.

56. *The Dogs in My Life* and *The Noble Wilds*, Aulacese (Vietnamese) edition, International Book Premiere in Nonthaburi, Thailand on August 15, 2009. SupremeMasterTV.com/bbs/tb.php/wow/386.

57. *The Secrets of Venus*, videoconference with Supreme Master TV staff in Los Angeles, USA on August 29, 2009. SupremeMasterTV.com/bbs/tb.php/bmd/636.

58. *Global Warming: Yes, There is a Solution!*, international conference in Lima, Peru on September 12, 2009. SupremeMasterTV.com/bbs/tb.php/wow/387.

59. Supreme Master Ching Hai's *The Dogs in My Life*, Spanish edition, international book premiere in Lima, Peru on September 12, 2009. SupremeMasterTV.com/bbs/tb.php/wow/400.

60. *Children's Health and Sustainable Planet*, international conference in Jeju Island, South Korea on September 21, 2009. SupremeMasterTV.com/bbs/tb.php/wow/379.

61. *Global Unity: Together in Saving Lives*, international conference in Hong Kong, China on October 3, 2009. SupremeMasterTV.com/bbs/tb.php/wow/383.

62. *Protect Our Home with L.O.V.E.*, international conference in Taichung, Formosa (Taiwan) on October 11, 2009. SupremeMasterTV.com/bbs/tb.php/wow/388.

63. Supreme Master Ching Hai's *The Noble Wilds*, German and French edition, *The Dogs in My Life*-Polish edition, international book premiere in Frankfurt, Germany on October 18, 2009. SupremeMasterTV.com/bbs/tb.php/wow/390.

64. *Vegan Organic for Prosperity and to Save the Planet from Climate Change*, international conference in Jakarta, Indonesia on October 22, 2009. SupremeMasterTV.com/bbs/tb.php/wow/393.

65. *Humanity's Leap into the Golden Era*, international conference in Washington DC, USA on November 8, 2009. SupremeMasterTV.com/bbs/tb.php/wow/397.

66. Supreme Master Ching Hai's video message to the Association of Mexican Magistrates Pro-Environment Justice and Interview by Country Focus on BBC Radio Wales on November 12, 2009. SupremeMasterTV.com/bbs/tb.php/wow/403.

67. *SOS-A Quick Action to Stop Global Warming Climate Change*, international conference in Orizaba, Veracruz, Mexico on November 16, 2009. SupremeMasterTV.com/bbs/tb.php/wow/411.

68. Interview with Supreme Master Ching Hai by the Irish Dog Journal on December 16, 2009. SupremeMasterTV.com/bbs/tb.php/wow/406.

69. *The Extraordinary Love and Immeasurable Wisdom of a Living Master*, teleconference with Supreme Master TV staff in Los Angeles, USA on August 1, 2010.

ADDITIONAL RESOURCES

Related Films

- *Home* (2009)
  A documentary by Yann Arthus-Bertrand that is almost entirely composed of aerial shots of various places on Earth. The film shows the diversity of life on the planet and how humanity is threatening its ecological balance. http://www.home-2009.com/us/index.html (also on Youtube)

- *Meat the Truth* (2007)
  Produced by the scientific bureau of the Party for the Animals, also known as the Nicolaas G. Pierson Foundation, this film reveals that the greatest cause of climate change is livestock farming for meat and dairy production, which produces more emissions than all the world's vehicles combined. Appearing in the film are renowned Dutch actors, writers and politicians, who share their views on being vegetarian. Scientific data from the United Nations Food and Agricultural Organization are also presented. www.partijvoordedieren.nl (Dutch) http://www.godsdirectcontact.org.tw/eng/news/194/vg_34.htm

- *An Inconvenient Truth* (2006)
  In this US Academy Award-winning documentary former Vice President of the United States, Al Gore, informs the public that global warming is a real and present danger. Based on leading-edge research from top scientists around the world, the movie describes how human activities over the past century could result in annihilation of our home planet, and that we have a small window of time to reverse this destructive trend so as to avert major global catastrophes such as extreme weather, floods, droughts, epidemics and heat waves beyond anything ever experienced. The film is a call to action for all of us to take responsibility and do our part.

- A *Delicate* Balance: *the Truth* (2007)
  This film goes further than Al Gore's *An Inconvenient Truth* by stating that the only hope for the planet is if people give up meat and dairy products. http://www.adelicatebalance.com.au/

- *The 11th Hour* (2007)

  A feature film documentary created, produced and narrated by Leonardo DiCaprio, describes the state of the natural environment and informs viewers that the present time is the last moment when change is possible. The film offers hope and potential solutions to environmental problems by calling for restorative action to reshape and rethink global human activity through technology, social responsibility and conservation. http://wwws.warnerbros.co.uk/11thhour; http://www.imdb.com/title/tt049293

- *Earthlings* (2005)

  This film, narrated by Academy Award nominee Joaquin Phoenix, describes humankind's dependence on animals for food, clothing, entertainment and use in research, but also illustrates our complete disrespect for animals. Through its in-depth study of pet stores, puppy mills, animal shelters, factory farms, the leather and fur trades, sports, the entertainment industry, medicine and science, *Earthlings* chronicles the day-to-day practices of some of the world's largest businesses, which rely on animals for profit. http://veg-tv.info/Earthlings (Also on Youtube)

- *Devour the Earth* (1995)

  This succinct documentary produced by the UK's Vegetarian Society and the European Vegetarian Union is narrated by world-renowned vegetarian and member of the Beatles Sir Paul McCartney. The film also features a prologue by the late president of Slovenia, Dr Janez Drnovsek. *Devour the Earth* clearly illustrates the environmental consequences of human activity and the effects of the meat-based diet on our beautiful, precious planet. http://www.youtube.com/watch?v=x420RF9AVk8 (Also on Youtube)

- Films on PETA.com:

  Click on "Meet Your Meat" and watch the educational videos (http://features.peta.org/VegetarianStarterKit/index.asp)

Related Links

SUPREMEMASTERTV.COM

Features programs on the green, healthy, compassionate organic vegan lifestyle and the topic of global warming. Featured broadcasts include live conferences on climate change, interviews with Nobel Prize laureates, NASA scientists, government leaders and environmental experts.

VEGSOURCE.COM

An excellent source for vegan recipes, educational videos, articles and books on the vegetarian lifestyle and animal-welfare topics.

IVU.ORG

The World Union of Vegetarian/Vegan Societies. Has promoted vegetarianism worldwide since 1908.

WORLDPRESERVATIONFOUNDATION.ORG

Materials and guidance to encourage individuals, the media, governments and other institutions to enact laws and policies that result in decreased consumption of animal products.

MERCYFORANIMALS.ORG
The official website of Mercy For Animals (MFA) offers information on animal-rights issues, an online store and more.

CHOOSEVEG.COM
The online edition of MFA's guide offering recipes, videos, tips and more.

EGGCRUELTY.COM
Photos, videos and information on MFA undercover investigations into animal cruelty at Ohio, USA egg farms.

VEGGUIDE.ORG
The ultimate restaurant and shopping guide for vegetarians and vegans.

GOVEG.COM
Resources for activists, news articles, hundreds of recipes and more.

VEGANHEALTH.ORG
Information on how to live a healthy, vegan lifestyle.

VIVA.ORG.UK
Through its popular campaigns, research, undercover exposés and effective media presentations, Viva! brings the reality of modern farming into people's living rooms.

INDEX

OUR PUBLICATIONS

To elevate our spirits and provide inspiration for daily living, a rich collection of The Supreme Master Ching Hai's teachings are available in the form of books, videotapes, audiotapes, music cassettes, DVDs, MP3s and CDs.

In addition to these published books and tapes, a wide array of Master's teachings can also be accessed quickly, free of charge from the Internet. For example, several websites feature the most recently published Supreme Master Ching Hai News magazine (see the "Quan Yin Web Sites" section below). Other featured online publications include Master's poetry and inspirational aphorisms, as well as lectures in the form of video and audio files.

BOOKS

Picking up one of Master's books in the middle of a busy day can be a lifesaver, as her words clearly remind us of our true Nature. Whether reading her spiritually informative lectures in The Key of Immediate Enlightenment series or the deeply compassionate poems contained in Silent Tears, gems of wisdom are always revealed.

In the list of books that follow, available volume numbers for each language are indicated in parentheses. For more information about obtaining these and other books, please see the "Obtaining Publications" section.

The Key of Immediate Enlightenment:
Aulacese(1-15), Chinese(1-10), English(1-5), French(1-2), Finnish(1), German(1-2), Hungarian(1), Indonesian(1-5), Japanese(1-4), Korean(1-11), Mongolian(1,6), Portuguese(1-2), Polish(1-2), Spanish(1-3), Swedish(1), Thai(1-6) and Tibetan(1)

The Key of Immediate Enlightenment-Questions and Answers:
Aulacese(14), Chinese(13), Bulgarian, Czech, English(12), French, German, Hungarian, Indonesian(13), Japanese, Korean(14), Portuguese, Polish and Russian(1)

Special Edition/Seven-Day retreat in 1992:
English and Aulacese

The Key of Immediate Enlightenment-Special Edition/1993 World Lecture Tour:
English (1-6) and Chinese (1-6).

Letters Between Master and Spiritual Practitioners:
English (1), Chinese (13), Aulacese (12), Spanish (1)

My Wondrous Experiences with Master:
Aulacese (12), Chinese (12)

Master Tells Stories:
English, Chinese, Spanish, Aulacese, Korean, Japanese and Thai.

Coloring Our Lives:
Chinese, English and Aulacese.

God Takes Care of Everything—Illustrated Tales of Wisdom from The Supreme Master Ching Hai:
Aulacese, Chinese, English, French, Japanese and Korean

The Supreme Master Ching Hai's Enlightening Humor —Your Halo Is Too Tight! Chinese and English.

Secrets to Effortless Spiritual Practice:
Chinese, English and Aulacese

God's Direct Contact—The Way to Reach Peace:
Chinese and English

Of God and Humans—Insights from Bible Stories:
Chinese and English.

The Realization of Health—Returning to the Natural and Righteous Way of Living: Chinese and English.

I Have Come to Take You Home:
Arabic, Aulacese, Bulgarian, Czech, Chinese, English, French, German, Greek, Hungarian, Indonesian, Italian, Korean, Mongolian, Polish, Spanish, Turkish, Romanian and Russian

Aphorisms:
Combined volume of Aulacese/English/Chinese, Spanish/Portuguese, French/German, Japanese/English, Korean/English, Chinese and English.

The Supreme Kitchen (1)—International Vegetarian Cuisine:
Combined volume of English/Chinese, Aulacese and Japanese

The Supreme Kitchen (2)—Home Taste Selections:
Combined volume of English/Chinese

One World... of Peace through Music:
Combined volume of English/Aulacese/Chinese.

A Collection of Art Creations by The Supreme Master Ching Hai:
English and Chinese

S.M. Celestial Clothes:
Combined volume in English and Chinese

The Dogs in My Life:
Aulacese, Chinese, English, Japanese, Korean, Spanish,
Polish and German

The Birds in My Life:
Aulacese, Chinese, English, French, Mongolian, German, Mongolian, Russian, Korean and
Indonesian

The Noble Wilds:
Aulacese, Chinese, English, French and German

Celestial Art:
Chinese and English

Thoughts on Life and Consciousness
A book by Dr. Janez Drnovšek: available in Chinese

POETRY COLLECTIONS

The Love of Centuries: A book of poems by Master
Available in English, Chinese, and Aulacese (Vietnamese)

Silent Tears: A book of poems by Master Available in English and Chinese

Wu Tzu Poems: A book of poems by Master
Available in Aulacese, Chinese and English

The Dream of a Butterfly: A book of poems by Master
Available in Aulacese, Chinese and English

Traces of Previous Lives: A book of poems by Master
Available in Aulacese, Chinese and English

The Old Time: A book of poems by Master
Available in Aulacese, Chinese and English.

Pebbles and Gold: A book of poems by Master
Available in Aulacese, Chinese and English

The Lost Memories: A book of poems by Master
Available in Aulacese, Chinese and English

Beyond the Realm of Time (song performance in Aulacese): CD and DVD
A Touch of Fragrance (song performance in Aulacese by celebrated singers): CD

That and This Day (poetry recitation in Aulacese): CD

Dream in the Night (song performance in Aulacese): CD and DVD

T-L-C, Please (song performance in Aulacese): CD

Please Keep Forever (poetry recitation in Aulacese): CD

Songs and Compositions of The Supreme Master Ching Hai: (CD) English, Aulacese, Chinese

The Song of Love: (DVD) Aulacese and English

Good Night Baby: (CD) in English

The Jeweled Verses (poems by distinguished Aulacese poets with recitation in Aulacese): CDs 1, 2 and DVDs 1, 2

The Golden Lotus (poetry recitation in Aulacese): CD and DVD

THE KEY OF IMMEDIATE ENLIGHTENMENT FREE SAMPLE BOOKLET

The Key of Immediate Enlightenment Sample Booklet presents an introduction to the teachings of Supreme Master Ching Hai. The availability of the Booklet in electronic form allows readers around the world to download it completely free of charge, or read it online wherever the Internet is accessible. From Afrikaans to Zulu, from Bengali to Urdu, in Macedonian, Malay and many others, this gem has been translated into over 74 languages.

In the Booklet Supreme Master Ching Hai emphasizes the importance of meditation in daily life. The text also includes Her discourses on the higher spiritual dimensions and the benefits of the vegan diet, as well as information on initiation into the Quan Yin Method of meditation, the ultimate and highest spiritual path. Supreme Master Ching Hai's uplifting insights in The Key of Immediate Enlightenment offer a bright ray of hope to those in quest of the Truth.

As Supreme Master Ching Hai states, "By attaining inner peace we will attain everything else. All the satisfaction, all the fulfillment of worldly and Heavenly desires comes from the Kingdom of God, the inner realization of our eternal harmony, our eternal wisdom and our almighty power. If we do not get these we never find satisfaction no matter how much money or power, or how high a position we have."

For direct access to the Sample Booklet, please visit:

http://sb.godsdirectcontact.net/

This website offers versions of Master's Sample Booklet in many languages. Join us in bringing the best gift to the world through sharing God's message and elevating human consciousness. If you find that your native or first language is not on our list and you would like to translate the Booklet into a language of your choice, please contact us at: divine@Godsdirectcontact.org.

Free Sample Booklet Download:

http://sb.godsdirectcontact.net (Formosa)

http://www.Godsdirectcontact.org/sample/ (U.S.A.)

http://www.direkterkontaktmitott.org/download/index.htm (Austria)

http://www.Godsdirectcontact.us/com/sb/

OBTAINING PUBLICATIONS

All publications are offered at near-cost prices. If you want to purchase or order a publication, please check first with your local Center or contact person for availability. To obtain a list of available publications, you can check with your local Center or visit the following website:

http://www.godsdirectcontact.org.tw/multilang/
http://smchbooks.com/new-c/cover/cover.htm
http://magazine.godsdirectcontact.net/

In addition, many of the online News magazine issues provide lists of recently released books and tapes.

If necessary, you may order directly from the headquarters in Formosa, address: P.O. Box 9, Hsihu, Miaoli, Formosa, ROC (36899). A detailed catalog is also available upon request.

QUAN YIN WWW SITES

God's direct contact—The Supreme Master Ching Hai International Association's global Internet site: http://www.Godsdirectcontact.org.tw/eng/links/links.htm

Access a directory of Quan Yin web sites worldwide, available to browse in many languages, as well as the 24-hour TV program, A Journey through Aesthetic Realms. You can download or subscribe to The Supreme Master Ching Hai News, available in eBook and printable formats. Multilingual editions of The Key of Immediate Enlightenment sample booklet are also available.

We invite you to listen to the recitation of Venerable Thich Man Giac's beautiful poetry through the melodious voice of Supreme Master Ching Hai, who also recites two of Her own poems, "Golden Lotus" and "Sayonara".

An Ancient Love (poetry recitation in Aulacese): CD and DVD

Traces of Previous Lives (poetry recitation in Aulacese): Audio tapes and CDs 1, 2 and 3, DVDs 1 and 2 (with subtitles in 17 languages)

A Path to Love Legends: Audio tapes and CDs 1, 2 and 3; video tapes 1 and 2 (poems by distinguished Aulacese poets; recitation in Aulacese)

* The poems "A Path to Love Legends," "An Ancient Love," "Beyond the Realm of Time," "Dream in the Night," "Please Keep Forever," "That and This Day," "Traces of Previous Lives," "The Jeweled Verses," "The Golden Lotus" and "T-L-C, Please" recited or set to music and sung by the poet herself.

Audio tapes, video tapes, MP3s, CDs and DVDs of The Supreme Master Ching Hai's lectures, music and concerts are available in Arabic, Armenian, Aulacese, Bulgarian, Cambodian, Cantonese, Chinese, Croatian, Czech, Danish, Dutch, English, Finnish, French, German, Greek, Hebrew, Hungarian, Indonesian, Italian, Japanese, Korean, Malay, Mandarin, Mongolian, Nepali, Norwegian, Persian, Polish, Portuguese, Russian, Sinhalese, Slovenian, Spanish, Swedish, Thai, Turkish and Zulu. Catalogs will be sent upon request. All inquiries are welcome.